DEDICATION

It's impossible for me to name all of the people who, in some way, helped me survive or cope with the effects of my stroke. From the first time I walked into the ER, until my last appointment, months later with the Outpatient Therapy facility, there were professional doctors, nurses, therapists, and technicians by my side. I will never forget their quick actions and timely words of support. But the Inpatient Therapy rehab facility, and all the staff that work there will always have a special place in my heart. If not for them, the road to recovery would have been a much slower and more challenging journey. It is a sure thing that collectively, they helped me not only regain most of what I had lost physically but helped shape the positive attitude that was necessary for me to deal with the many daunting challenges that come with having a stroke. But there is one man whose positive impact on my recovery and survival is too amazing to accurately describe. That man, who I will refer to as Dr. D, is the attending provider at the Inpatient rehab facility. From the day I first arrived at the facility until the day I was discharged, he was a shining light guiding me down the path to recovery. Every weekday at approximately 8:00 AM he checked up on me. He patiently calmed me down in those first days when I was frantic with worry and bubbling over with anger at the unfairness of it all. He patiently answered every foolish and paranoid question I had during those early days when I was most vulnerable mentally, He addressed and promptly resolved the legitimate medical concerns I had during my stay. But above all, when he visited me during those early mornings each Monday through Friday, he made me feel I was the only patient under his care, and he would therefore walk the extra mile, just like his staff, to provide me with whatever it took to help me make as full a recovery as hard work would allow me. He was my rock, and along with my life partner Patty, who was always at my side and whose love surrounded me, and made what had happened to me more bearable, he was the one who took away the stress and worry that might have otherwise consumed me.

CONTENT

ACKNOWLEDGMENTS

The first thing I need to make clear is that I have purposely left out the name of the hospital, inpatient and outpatient facility as well as the names of the individuals that helped me deal with my stroke. In addition to many of the individuals wishing to remain anonymous, there is the fact that there are outstanding hospitals, inpatient and outpatient programs, doctors, nurses, therapists, and technicians in every corner of our country who will provide the same level of care that I received. I believe I would have received the same level of care in hundreds of locations in the U.S., and in many other countries around the world. The most important thing to me is that caregivers at all levels suggest that their patients, still reeling from having a life-altering stroke, obtain and read a copy of this book, so they have some idea of what happens to them next, both physically and emotionally; as they start down the road to recovery. I sincerely wish that every person on the planet, not educated in stroke symptoms and treatment at a professional level, would obtain and read a copy of this book. And, I think that my wish will be more easily achieved if any hospital or medical professional can hand out a generic copy of my Stroke Survivor story versus one filled with the name of a facility other than theirs, and personnel other than those that work in their organization.

The second thing I wish to make clear is that

when I entered the hospital, I was given quite a bit of information to educate me on strokes, and the many factors associated with them, for which I was extremely grateful. However, what I did not receive, which would have especially helped me during those early days, was a first-hand account of someone who had actually had a stroke. A blow-by-blow account of how they dealt with it mentally while they were being stabilized in critical care, and the additional obstacles they might have to face, such as swallowing, depending on what areas of their body were impacted by the stroke. A first-hand perspective of starting the long path of rehab and the wonderful, dedicated people they would meet along the way. The unbelievable professionalism and supportive nature of the Occupational, Physical, and Speech Therapists they would work with. And maybe more than anything, the fact that it was only human to fall into those "why me" moments, and that the important thing was to keep fighting. A book or other form of first-hand account like that would have really helped me deal with the reality of my situation by "seeing" it through the eyes of someone else who had been where I was now.

And, the third thing I wish to make clear, is that I must really apologize for the term "Diary" in the title of this book. In fact, although there is an entry for each day during the first few months of my stroke, as well as a dated entry for a few updates, I sometimes switch from past tense to present tense as I expand on things that happened on a particular day, so you the reader, will have a better understanding of what was going on, or what I was thinking at any particular moment. I hope my additional comments are helpful to you,

Also, some of the content of the first few pages of this book refer to my "healthy lifestyle." Although the way I tried to maximize my health is not directly related to my stroke, I do believe that we all should practice a healthy lifestyle as a matter of course. It certainly didn't prevent me having my first stroke, but I'm convinced it helped me stave off other potential medical problems.

The truth is that I am a bit obsessive about healthy living and I preach to my family, friends, and business associates constantly about taking care of their bodies and making sure they followed a healthy diet. And I practiced what I preached. I was an extremely fit guy, who got a good night's sleep every night, didn't smoke or drink, and who worked out hard 3 times a week plus played several hours of competitive tennis, every week. In addition, I ate right, stayed away from fatty foods, hadn't been to a fast-food restaurant in years, and had a low resting heartrate, low blood pressure, and normal fasting blood sugar. I got an extremely thorough physical every summer around my birthday, by my Primary Care Physician that included extensive bloodwork, Cognitive Testing, Cologuard Testing, Spirometry Testing, an EKG, and Peripheral Vascular Testing. And the overall results have been consistently normal since I had the first of these thorough physicals more than ten years ago. In fact, the results have consistently indicated that I have the body and overall health of a man younger than I am. So, for me at least, leading a kind of "preventive lifestyle" didn't prevent the stroke, but undoubtedly helped me deal with its effect on me, and definitely gave me the residual strength to recover quicker, by months, than what is considered normal. I've had input from a variety of medical professionals as well as rehab professionals who have all told me that I've recovered at an unusually fast pace. It's also possible that if I hadn't lived a preventive lifestyle, I might have had a stroke 20 years ago, or not survived the one I did have.

More important than my almost obsessive focus on fitness and overall health was a simple fact that, due to my staying current with what was required to lead a healthy lifestyle I was fortunate to know quite a bit more about stroke symptoms than the average person. That additional knowledge caused me to move much faster than I might have otherwise, since my symptoms were not the classic symptoms that most people have a passing knowledge of, such as slurred speech, a feeling of disorientation, or balance issues. In fact, as you will soon see, my symptoms were quite a bit different than the more well-known ones I just listed. And, I now wonder, as a stroke survivor, if the "average" person had access to a book like this one, would reading it help them seek medical attention sooner when they experienced unusual symptoms which were not readily identified as those of a stroke.

If you are reading this book, chances are good that you have suffered and survived a stroke. A fair amount of the information in the following pages will hopefully help you understand what is coming if you are soon to be headed to rehab. If for some reason you choose not to go straight from the hospital to an inpatient rehab facility, I beg you to reconsider. I believe you have an infinitely better chance to recover if you enter a good inpatient facility and allow the professionals to do their job. It certainly worked for me. As far as this book, the information contained within may help you prepare for rehab, but more importantly, if you get your family, especially your grown children, and friends to read it, you may help prevent one of them from ever saying "If I had only known."

1. THE STROKE

Day One. I got up around 7:00, took a long, hot shower, prepared my morning cup of coffee and bowl of oatmeal and sat down to eat my normal breakfast. After I finished eating, I got dressed in my "work from home" uniform of a t-shirt and jeans and headed for my home office. I was looking forward to spending a quiet day working on the software application my company was about to bring to market. About two hours later, a little after 10:00, I was cruising along, typing at my usual frantic pace, when I suddenly noticed that I was no longer getting the correctly spelled words in the document on my computer screen that my mind was telling my fingers to type. I was seeing a lot of spelling errors. I was definitely confused about what was happening, and the more I tried to understand, the more I became scared, since whatever it was had to be linked to my brain. As soon as the word "brain" popped into my head, I thought stroke. I had never heard of symptoms of stroke that involved typing, but I would be the first to admit that I certainly didn't know as much about stroke symptoms, as I should. Compared to, say, heart attack symptoms, which I felt I knew a lot about. So, I immediately called my significant other, Patty, and asked her to rush home and take me to the ER of a nearby hospital. She left work immediately and had me to the hospital within 20 minutes. Patty and I walked into the ER about 11:00 AM, at which time we announced what was happening to me and were immediately taken to an exam room. At this point I could still walk, freely move my arms, and speak normally. The ER Doctor examined me and asked me a series of questions, such as, "What is your name? Do you know what day it is? Do you know what year you were born?" I was still speaking normally, but was beginning to feel sightly disoriented. I was taken to Radiology for a CT scan. As soon as that was done, the hospital had a room ready for me and I was taken there. Within 15 minutes a hospital doctor came into the room and told me I was having an Ischemic stroke. An ischemic stroke is one where a blood clot within my blood vessels is blocking blood flow to part of my brain. The doctor also told me that they didn't want to give me the chemical they used to dissolve clots because there were other clots in my brain they wanted to protect. She told us that they wanted to do a Thrombectomy on me to break up the clot manually but did not have anyone on staff who was capable of doing the procedure, so they had arranged for an ambulance to take me to another nearby hospital where there was a surgeon who could do the procedure. At this point I could still walk, and my arms still moved freely. The ambulance arrived shortly thereafter, and the driver and helper loaded me aboard and we left. We arrived at the second hospital and were met by a Nurse Practitioner on staff there. The next few hours were a blur to me. Later I found out that I had been checked into a room in the Critical Care unit. My right side was now paralyzed. I remember being in the room and trying with all my willpower for what seemed like hours, to wiggle my right index finger and having no success. When it came time to administer my medications, I was given several new medications including Famotidine, Atorvastatin, and a new drug called Brilinta, all of which should, together, prevent further strokes.

Day Two. I was visited by a neurologist and his assistant. He told me that I had suffered an acute left-sided pontine stroke. My pontine stroke had affected part of my brain stem called the pons. Although I had difficulty swallowing some balance issues, and paralysis of the entire right side of my body, it could have been even worse, since if I would have had the stroke on the back of my pons, I may have experienced ataxia, a condition where I couldn't control my muscles. I also could have had a stroke in my brain stem that caused vertigo and double vision, or a really bad one that affected my blood pressure, heart rate, or even my ability to breath. My pontine stroke could have even caused me to develop a condition called Locked-in Syndrome (LiS), where my entire body may have been paralyzed. To say I got off lightly is stretching it, but it could have been worse. As soon as he explained what had happened to me, the doctor immediately examined me and confirmed that I was paralyzed on my right side and that I could not even squeeze his fingers with my right hand. He then explained that the Thrombectomy was a very dangerous procedure and that he wanted to wait. He told us he had put me on a very aggressive series of medications, and he wanted to wait and see how they worked. Even in my disoriented condition, it was obvious to me that the medication protocol the neurologist had put me on was to prevent me having another stroke. I could not fault his decision, but the effects of my current stroke, the paralysis, the slurred speech, and the difficulty swallowing were not going to go away and were all something I would have to deal with. At that time, I was thinking about the stroke and all the parts of my life it would change, and I thought, with a heavy dose of mental sarcasm, "the only bit of good luck I've received so far is that I'm left-handed." I'd find out as time went on that I was indeed lucky to be left-handed. Right then I snapped back to a positive mental outlook and remembered all the times over the years that I'd had serious sports injuries like broken L4 and L5 vertebrae, a herniated disk, or a torn MCL. So far, I had beaten all those injuries and worked my way back to normal every single time. I began looking at my stroke the same way. I was going to beat it. I knew it would take longer and be much harder, and I knew I'd be in big trouble if I didn't start dedicating myself to extremely hard, intense rehab, and doing whatever it took to work myself back, as close as possible, to my former self. So, to have something to shoot for, I set a goal right then that exactly one year from yesterday, I would be back on the tennis court and in good enough condition to play two full sets. Now I just had to find out how to do it. Sometime later Saturday morning, I was again visited by the same Registered Nurse, who was very cordial, and seemed to really take an interest in how I was holding up. I told her that I had very little interest in eating since I seemed to cough everything right back up. She emphasized that building my strength was one of the most important things I could do right now, and to follow the Speech Therapists instructions and make sure I ate all the food that was given me. Ironically, just a few minutes later, I was visited by a Speech Therapist who told me that she was there because the stroke and resultant paralysis, in addition to affecting my speech, had also affected my ability to swallow, and she was going to help me overcome the challenge of swallowing to make sure I didn't aspirate food or liquid into my lungs and develop Pneumonia. She first told Patty and I to make sure I only ate when I was alert and in an upright position, and to take very small bites of food and sips of water. She had me sip from a glass and noted that liquid spilled out of the right side of my mouth due to my facial paralysis, so we switched to a straw, which worked much better. She also had me do breathing exercises, to increase breath support, which immediately helped with both my swallowing, and my speech patterns. As far as helping me speak more precisely, she had me do an exercise where I repeated, several times, phrases and sentences containing multi-syllable words. We would isolate and work on the words I had trouble with, and repeat the exercise. I noted improvement in my speech every time. This session came at the perfect time and was of great value to me, since I discovered at lunch that day, which would be the first real meal I would try to eat in its entirety since my arrival, how hard it was to sip water or nibble on crackers without coughing, especially if I got distracted or didn't concentrate, so I made sure to follow her instructions to the letter. I still didn't eat much of my meal though because of the difficulty swallowing and resultant coughing spells that occurred despite following her directions. Learning to eat and drink again were just going to take some time. When it came time to dispense my medications, everything went well.

Day Three. I met once more with the RN and told her I was eating better due to my Speech Therapy sessions, plus I was starting to get the slightest feeling back in my right hand. Again, ironically, a short time later I was taken to the X-Ray Department where the staff X-Rayed me drinking a variety of drinks of varying viscosity as well as chewing and swallowing light foods such as crackers. The technicians took X-Rays of me performing these tasks and put the entire period of me trying different drinks and foods on video for me to watch. It was tremendously educational and helpful to see an X-Ray of myself actually swallowing, since I was having trouble swallowing anything, and the video helped me see the right and wrong way to do it. Right then I thought to myself, "these folks think of everything. This video is amazingly helpful." I watched the video closely, multiple times, when it came to the parts where I had trouble. When I did it wrong, I could clearly see whatever liquid or solid I was trying to swallow going into my lung opening instead of my esophagus. When we finished, I was wheeled back to my room. Everything was relatively routine for the rest of the day and evening. Later that day, Patty and I had a visit from a representative for several rehab facilities associated with the hospital, who reviewed with us all the rehab programs at the various facilities and asked us if we would like to start my rehab at one of them. He then explained that it would be three hours per day, Monday through Friday. One hour with a Speech Therapist. one hour with an Occupational Therapist, and one hour with a Physical Therapist. My answer was "yes," and I wanted to start as soon as possible. There was one facility that the representative had mentioned, that my Primary Care Doctor, who I trusted completely, had given very high marks for exceptional patient care and that was good enough for me. The representative told us they would have to work out the details with my insurance company, which was not open on Sunday, but there was a bed opening up at that facility the following Wednesday, and they would plan on moving me to that facility on that day. I was extremely excited to be starting concentrated rehab so soon and couldn't wait until Wednesday arrived. Sometime during the afternoon, I was visited by two Physical Therapists who got me up and into a special walker that I stood in, with special padded arms to rest my forearms and hands on. Since my right hand was still paralyzed, they had to strap it to the walker. The two then assisted me as I tried to walk a small part of the hallway outside my room. Due to my paralysis, one of them had to manually move my right leg, and I remember how amazed I was that a little walk like this exhausted me. Also, that day, I was visited by a Speech Therapist who diligently worked with me to practice speaking, drinking, and swallowing. I found those sessions very useful and must say that their department seemed extremely motivated to help me.

Day Four. Today the same RN as the day before paid her morning visit to me and told me that I was doing fine and that she was adjusting my medications to address the insomnia episodes I had experienced from time to time during my stay. She stressed once again to eat everything on my meal trays for strength. I had another visit from the Speech Therapy staff that afternoon, and their lessons and motivated behavior were something I looked forward to each day. I especially looked forward to it today since I had been afraid to talk to my children, all of whom lived literally thousands of miles away, for the first few days, because of my slurred speech. Patty had been talking to them all daily, and keeping them appraised of how I was doing, but tonight I would be talking to them for the first time since the stroke and I wanted to sound as good as possible. So, during that entire session we concentrated on me speaking slowly and focusing on proper enunciation. I also had another visit from the Physical Therapists, and another walk down the hallway in the special walker they provided for me. This time we made twice the distance with half the rest breaks we had needed the day before. I remember considering something as minor as that to be a victory. That evening I talked with my children, and although I spoke slower than usual, I was happy with all four conversations and felt I had assured them that I was on the road to recovery. They all were prepared to fly in to support me, but I convinced them that with my upcoming move to a rehab center I would be in session for a good part of each day, and I would feel better if they waited a few weeks. I told them I would be calling every day, and Patty had already been providing them with voice and text updates from day one, so they could easily track my progress. They grudgingly agreed to delay their flights for a few weeks.

Day Five. This morning I had a breakthrough! I was finally able to move my right index finger, which was a big victory for me at the time. Later that morning I was visited again by the representative of the various rehab facilities. He told me that they were still talking with my insurance company about how many days my insurance would cover while I was in rehab, and the two parties had not settled on a number yet. He said that my Day Six transfer might slide one extra day at most if they didn't quickly come to an agreement with the insurance company. That was not the news I wanted to hear, and I remember being quite a bit down, mentally, because of it. I was really motivated to start aggressive rehab as soon as possible, so I could work my way back to my former life, and even one more day in Critical Care felt like a setback. I was finding out quickly, as a new stroke survivor, that I had become much more emotional, to the point where I tended to grab on to any positive thing that was going to happen in my life, with great anticipation, no matter how insignificant it would be to a normal person. And I was more disillusioned than that same normal person would be when that positive thing was delayed or didn't happen. That's how I felt now, but I was powerless to do anything about it except focus on my own rehab program right there in the room, the sole purpose of which was to make my entire right-hand move more and become stronger. I focused on moving the right hand for hours and was rewarded by finally getting some of my other fingers to move. Another victory to build on. Later I spent some more time with a Speech Therapist, working on my speech and swallowing technique, at which time the therapist informed me that I was ahead of schedule in both swallowing technique and my speech. This was more good news for me, because I also believed the daily therapy with them had made talking and swallowing much easier than when I first arrived. It was nice to have my observations confirmed.

Day Six. When I awoke today, after a full night's sleep due to the adjustment of my medications, I felt energized. For the first time since my arrival, I didn't feel tired. I spent the majority of my day inventing little exercise programs for my hand and foot, while lying in bed. The good news was that I was starting to have movement in my right leg and my right arm. And this was in addition to now being able to slightly move all four fingers and thumb on my right hand. I still had no movement in my shoulder or foot though. I had my normal visit with the RN, who I had really come to like for her sense of humor and efforts to lighten my mood. I showed her the increased movement I had in my right hand and fingers, and she told me I was progressing faster than normal and that was a good sign. Later that day I had another session with a Speech Therapist, and it was obvious to us both that, due to my sessions with them, I was handling speaking and swallowing much better than when I arrived. Another small victory for me. I also had another visit from the rehab facilities representative, telling me that the final arrangements were being made with the insurance company and that I would be moving for sure on Day Seven. He told me at that time that I would be an inpatient at the rehab facility for approximately 30 days. He also told me that both the Occupational Therapist and Physical Therapist assigned to me had already looked at my profile and discovered that I was extremely fit prior to the stroke, and might still have enough residual strength for them to push me a little harder. I was extremely happy to hear this, and tremendously motivated not to let them down. Then I was told that when I was ready to leave the rehab center, I would be totally evaluated by a staff

M.D, Speech, Occupational, and Physical Therapist, to see if I was rehabilitated to the point where I could start at an Outpatient Therapy facility. If any of them felt I wasn't ready, more days would be added to my stay. How many more days my insurance company would pay was still in discussion. When it came time to dispense my medications, everything went well, and I was out by 9:30.

Day Seven. I awoke this morning totally pumped because I was moving to the rehab facility. That move had become the most important thing in my life. I was ready to start working as hard as it took to get as much of my normal life back as humanly possible. About lunchtime one of the nurses came in and confirmed that I would be leaving for the Outpatient Therapy facility in about two hours or so. Shortly after that I had one last visit from a Speech Therapist. She informed me that she was going to do a "Cranial Nerve Oral Mechanism Exam on me to assess the function and structure of my face mouth, and throat. She had me open and close my mouth and slide my jaw back and forth to show facial sensation and jaw control, although she did note decreased movement on the right side of my face when I smiled, puckered or rounded my lips, or puffed out my cheeks. And, I did have some problems when saying "ah." I told the therapist that my voice was not as clear and intent as it was prior to the stroke. After she had finished her exam, I spent virtually all my waiting time working my hand as best I could. At about 4:00 in the afternoon, a nurse came in and informed me that it would be a few more hours before I left due to some last-minute issues that had come up at the Outpatient Therapy facility. I was a bit sad even for that small delay, but was happy that she had taken the time to update me, otherwise I know I would have been convinced that something bad had happened, and that my move to another location would be delayed again. The stroke had definitely done something to my emotions, since I wore them on my sleeve much more than before. Finally, at around 5:30, the nurse came in and, after apologizing again for the delay, told me it was time to check out. I was so relieved that my fear of another delay was not going to come true that I had completely forgotten about my unjustified paranoia by the time she settled me in the wheelchair. The trip to Outpatient Therapy was uneventful, and I was successfully checked into my new room. Within ten minutes I was indoctrinated by one of the staff nurses, who was very cordial and stayed 5 – 10 minutes extra, chatting with me. I couldn't help thinking, "if everyone is like this nurse and the Therapists I've been told about, I definitely have come to the right rehab facility." The "patient fall directive" was in place at this facility as well, so I spent the next hours of my time in the room either sitting on an alarmed chair or buzzing the nurse's station to get someone to help me move to the alarmed bed. So, I had to buzz for someone to assist me if I wanted to move from bed to chair or get up for any other reason. Fine with me! The hospital had had the same directive. About 8:30 a nurse came in to review my medication list and ask me if I was in any pain, since they could address that immediately with Tylenol or even Tramadol. My medication list was 100% accurate, and I wasn't in any pain, so that period went quickly. I'd had contact with two people so far and was very impressed by how personable they were. As the days went by, I was to find that everybody at the facility was like that. They would all go the extra mile to help their patient's stay at their facility be just a little easier. The nurse came by to dispense my medications and it was then lights out with the door closed. What a delight. The place, by 9:00, was as quiet as it could be. I was looking forward to a good night's sleep because my first therapy session with my Occupational Therapist was at 7:00 AM the next morning.

2. MY STAY AT INPATIENT REHAB

Day Eight. I woke up at 6:00 in anticipation of my 1st session with my Occupational Therapist (OT) for the next 30 days. Promptly at 7:00 the OT knocked on my door. She then helped me into my wheelchair and wheeled me into the actual working area of the facility, which was full of equipment used in various parts of their programs. The first thing she let me know was that her job was to prepare me for life outside of rehab. This included learning how to dress, how to go to the bathroom, how to shower, how to tie my shoes and the myriad other things people who haven't had a stroke take for granted. In addition, she was going to help me get my right shoulder, arm, wrist, hand, and fingers working again. She said that a lot of the exercises we would do in the coming weeks were part of my "Neuromuscular re-education." She told me that my brain would grow new neural pathways to my right side but that we would have to educate them, mainly through repetitive motions. We would teach them how to activate the muscles in my legs, and how to have them "fire" in the right order, so that I would walk correctly. We would also teach my hand and fingers how to do both simple and complex tasks, by repeating them over and over. The first thing the OT did was have me warm up my upper body by doing mild exercises and stretches. Then we started right in on finding out what my right side was capable of. We also tried a number of finger dexterity tests where she timed me to

24

completion of the task. The OT had me stack 10 cones on a table directly in front of me by grabbing them only with my right hand and moving them to form a stack on my left. Then she had me take the cones from that stack and form a new one on my right. I was able to struggle through 2 cycles. She also worked on rotating my shoulder in all directions, doing 4 sets of 10 reps up and down and side to side, while she held me in place, to increase my Range of Motion (ROM). We also concentrated, during the last 30 minutes, on different ways to increase my grip strength, such as twisting and bending into a U-Shape, a Red (lower resistance) FlintRehab Resistance Bar (Hand and Forearm Exerciser), and squeeze small hand exercisers. I do remember that my right hand was so weak and swollen that I could only exert 20 pounds of force when I tried to squeeze a special digital hand gauge the OT had. This was compared to easily exerting 110 pounds of force when I used my good left hand. So, on Day Eight, my right-hand grip was less than 20% of my left. Now I had a new short-term goal to shoot for. I would triple my right-handed grip strength, taking it to 60 pounds of force, by the time six months had elapsed since my stroke. I didn't know whether that was a realistic time frame or not, but I was going to try my hardest to achieve that goal. We stopped at 8:00 so I could go back to my room to eat breakfast.

Finally, it was time for the OT to hand me off to my Physical Therapist (PT). She introduced herself and said that she would be the one to help me get my strength and balance back, and the one who would ultimately teach me how to walk again. But first, like the OT, she evaluated me to establish a starting point. Before she tested me in any area, she fitted my right foot and ankle with an ankle-foot orthosis (AFO), while still in my room, which she secured with an ace wrap. An AFO is a hard brace worn on the lower leg that improves overall walking safely and efficiency for people with little or no control over their foot due to paralysis resulting from their stroke. She secured it with a non-slip sock. Then she tested it by having me sit in the chair in my room and then stand. Then repeating the process. I used only my right arm if I needed to balance. I was able to do 5 of the sit-and-stand exercises. We then went into one of the therapy rooms. The PT started my session on an Elliptical. This is a great machine to warm me up my entire body. When I started, we had to use a Velcro strap to keep my weak right hand attached to the right handle, and an attachment had to be placed on my right leg to keep it in an upright position and not falling away to my right. I remember this was the day where I started concentrating on using my right arm and leg on the Elliptical as much as possible, to make them stronger, rather than putting most of the load on my left arm and leg, which were not affected by the stroke. After warming up, the PT did several more tests on me including, having me slide my right heel back and forth to determine my right leg strength and ROM, having me attempt to lay on my back and bridge, which I was able to do, having me lay on my left side and raise my right leg, I was only able to do it 5 times before running out of gas. She then had me lie prone on my elbows and try to do a modified push-up, I was able to do 5 of these before running out of gas. We also did an exercise where I stood at the base of a set of stairs. I grabbed the railing with my right hand with assistance from a 2nd therapist, and then, with my PT squatting on the steps above me, instantly ready to move if I lost my balance, she had me step up onto the first step with my right leg, to help strengthen it.

I remember one test just as the session was ending, where I lay face down on an elevated table, and, while lying flat, tried to lift my right foot off the table by simply bending my right knee. I could only do a couple of reps, and even those few I did do accomplished very little. I was only able to raise my right foot 2" to 3" off the table. In a sudden storm of anger and frustration I remember thinking, "two weeks ago I was squatting 280 pounds in the gym and now I can't even lift my own leg. Regaining my former strength is going to take a miracle!" I nearly broke down in tears right then, but forced those thoughts back into the dark place they came from and stayed in the moment. If I was going to have even a remote chance of a full recovery, I had to make sure I heard everything my PT said. In this instance, her words brought me back from the edge. She was very supportive and said that virtually all new stroke patients experienced the same thing with their leg that was affected by the stroke, when they first started their recovery, since their brain was in the process of making new neural pathways. She looked me right in the eyes and said, "growing new neural pathways takes time. Don't you give up." Her words gave me hope, which was exactly what I needed at that specific moment in time. The last few minutes of the session we had me use a walker to try to walk, with my PT and another therapist right beside me for safety. Both my PT and I noticed right away that when I tried to take a step, I consistently dragged the toe of my right foot, occasionally hyperextended my right knee, and at times had a scissored gait where my knees and thighs were crossing each other while I was trying to walk. It's caused by the muscles responsible for bringing the thighs together not working right. The session ended then, but as my PT wheeled me back to my room, she continued to talk to me. She was adamant when she told me, "You will get better. Don't let your weakness right now depress you. By the time you're ready to leave, you will walk out of here." I remember thinking as she wheeled me to my room, "She believes what she just said to me with absolute certainty, I will work until I drop to help her get me on my feet again. She is a positive treatment all by herself." Later that day I was visited by a new Speech Therapist (ST). The time with her was totally enjoyable as we worked on my speech and swallowing. But it was practical too, because I still had too many coughing incidents due to improper swallowing, and each session with the ST refined the proper technique a little more, which helped reduce the number of incidents. During the ST session, I once again had a "Cranial Nerve Oral Mechanism Exam to establish a new baseline. She had me once again open and close my mouth and slide my jaw back and forth, and again noted decreased movement on the right side of my face when I smiled, puckered or rounded my lips, or puffed out my cheeks. Also, she had me do my best to pronounce the letters "b, s, f, v, and t, and the word ah." I had trouble with most of the letters as well as saying "ah."

Day Nine and Ten. I discovered very quickly that on the weekends I was pretty much on my own with too much time to think. That first weekend I tried to rest and spent most of each day in my room with Patty. One of the key things she provided, besides moral support, was a thorough massage of my right foot and lower leg. My right foot was a little swollen and slightly discolored, although not enough to require medical attention. Patty massaged it every evening. It became almost an instant ritual, and routine part of her daily visits. In less than five minutes of gentle massage, the swelling went away, and the foot returned to its normal color. As the staff got to know us, some would jokingly tell her, "You're spoiling him. Once word gets around, there will be a line of people outside the door wanting a foot rub too."

This type of light bantering was great for me

since it helped me stay in a positive place, mentally, which I desperately needed to be in if I was going to continue to recover. It was very easy during that first weekend, and subsequent weekends to a lesser degree, with so much idle time on my hands, to slip into a "my life is over, what's the use in rehabbing at all" mentality, resulting in extreme anger. Anger which consumed me for short periods of time and made it impossible for those around me to keep me focused on anything positive, like healing and getting my life back to normal. When I had these episodes, which came out of nowhere, I made it clear that Patty could take her Rah-Rah, "life back to normal" speech and shove it. My exact words were," give those stupid dreams to someone who believes in fairy tales, not to me." And 15 minutes later I would snap out of it, totally embarrassed, and apologize. Then, possibly 4-5 hours later the same thing would happen again. Everyone knew it was a side effect of the stroke, but that does nothing to make the situation less stressful. This was especially hard on Patty since she had never seen me like this. After a couple of these episodes, I knew that I had to keep my mind occupied to prevent it from happening again. I really tried to focus on my victories and how quickly I was improving, rather than how my life used to be. I told Patty what I was trying to do, and without a 2nd thought she bought in to helping me find a way to stay focused on victories only. She was amazing from that point forward because she had an uncanny way of turning a small victory on my part into an hour-long story. And it was a story I could hear her tell over-and-over, without ever becoming bored. She quickly became an expert at bolstering my overall mood and stopping my dark mood dead in its tracks. My mood was also bolstered further during that first long weekend, as well as subsequent weekends, when several of the weekend staff stopped by my room and let me know that they would be more than happy to take me for hallway rides, or, in the coming week's, walks, if I felt up to it, to give me a little exercise and a small break up of my day. In the coming weeks, as I graduated from wheelchair, to walker, to cane, to unassisted baby steps, those hallway walks on the weekends became one more thing for me to look forward to. With the cane especially, the more I got to practice the better. Actually, that first weekend I had asked for and received permission to, with a little assistance from the staff, rig the legs of the chair in my room, the bed frame, and even the base of the tray table with some rubber exercise bands given to me by my OT and PT. I was allowed to do this as long as I didn't get off the alarmed chair or bed, try to stand or walk, and pushed my call button for assistance whenever I wanted to move. I was as concerned about my safety as the staff, so I promised I would not abuse the privilege they had given me. Safety first! I also had Patty bring a spring-loaded hand grip I had used at home, prior to my stroke, so I could use it, along with my Red FlintRehab Resistance Bar to work on strengthening my right hand and wrist. By the time I was done, I had a mini gym in my room that allowed me to safely stretch and exercise my fingers, hand, leg, and foot while I was sitting in the chair or laying on the bed. My mini gym setup was such that I easily stayed within the rehab center's rules, but it was very effective.

The work I did on the weekends was partially the cause, along with all the supervised hard work I did during the week, that helped me increase the movement of my fingers, hand, and foot. But though I tried endlessly, I could still barely move the toes and front part of my right foot upward, even an inch. When I wasn't working the bands, I got cabin fever very quickly and it got to the point, even with Patty there, where any break in the "routine" was unusually exciting to me. One of the things that accomplished that was the meals. I was on a cardiac diet, with all food arriving chopped or mashed to address my swallowing problem. I got another indication of the facility staff's willingness to help make my stay as enjoyable as possible on that first weekend. I was working hard each day on the bands set up in my room, and the Red FlintRehab Resistance Bar, and as a result I was very hungry at mealtime. Saturday night's dinner was a lasagna dish I really enjoyed, but I was still hungry after I had eaten it all. I jokingly mentioned to Patty that their portions were way too small for a hard-working guy like me, while a staff member was present, and five minutes later the staff member brought me in a 2nd helping, chopped and mashed like the first dinner. She did it without me asking her directly, and I was impressed at her kindness and unsolicited effort to help me. That weekend I also quickly became best friends with applesauce since it was the perfect consistency for me to swallow without incident. I was taking so many pills now that applesauce was also used to help me swallow them all. A few crushed pills with a teaspoon of applesauce, was very effective.

I couldn't help but wonder, other than my sudden bursts of anger and occasional periods of outright despair, how much the stroke had affected my emotional state in more subtle ways, because getting excited over the approach of lunch or dinner was unlike the old me, and my love affair with applesauce was completely unlike the old me. But then, again, flying off the handle during short periods of uncontrollable anger was completely unlike me. That first weekend I started to face the hard reality that I really had experienced brain damage, and only time would tell what subtle changes it had made in my personality. The overriding thing that I held onto at that time was that all my regular mental faculties seemed to be working just fine, including being able to recall all my memories. Patty also pointed out that first Sunday that I hadn't lost my sharp wit, or my self-deprecating sense of humor. That was good news since I had always used both of those traits to great success while running my Software Development business, and both of those traits made my relationship with all three therapists much more pleasant than if I had become a grumpy old man.

So, gradually, however, I got a handle on it. I had enough contact with my doctors, OT, PT, and ST, where I was WARNED that this emotional rollercoaster could happen. I KNEW what was happening to me. I KNEW, without a doubt, that these kinds of attitudes, either mindless anger or overwhelming despair would consume me, little by little. And, finally, I KNEW my spirit and thought process well enough that I also knew that for me the only answer was all out attack. I kept reminding myself of my overall goal to be playing tennis again on the one-year anniversary of this stroke, and how I WAS going to make it. In a way, by the time I completed those first few weeks, I was able to channel my anger into a positive thing. I focused my anger into declaring war on my stroke. Roll your eyes all you want. It worked. During my last few weeks at the Inpatient Rehab Center, I never again lost control of the anger I had locked up inside myself. I focused it entirely on my declaration of war. My enemy was the stroke that had taken a good part of my life from me. The only way I could win the war was to get back what I had lost. So, I had to use my anger to enhance the rehabbing of my body. It would be on Day 19 and Day 22 before I found a way to do that. Before I found two perfect "battlefields." Places where I could both use my anger and outrage to attack my stroke and take rehab to a higher level.

Day Eleven. My first therapy session at 7:00 AM each day was with my OT, and my OT was at my door promptly at 7:00, ready to go. The first thing I did was show her my weekend mini gym. She was impressed at my ingenuity but cautioned me that I was in a significantly weakened state, and not to perform much exercise before our therapy times during the week. I needed all my strength and endurance to maximize those planned sessions. She then asked me if I had any difficulty going to the bathroom or dressing myself. At that early stage, with a seriously weakened right arm and leg, and a seriously weakened right hand grip, I had to admit to her that I did. My big problem while going to the bathroom was lowering and raising my underwear and sweatpants using only my left hand and actually getting up from the toilet to pull them up. My OT showed me a few ways to address these issues, including making sure I used the bars on the wall to perform a "pull to stand" technique to safely stand, and then simplify the process of my clothing by pulling my underwear alone up to my knee and then from that point forward to focus on keeping the elastic waistband straight and inching it up to my hips very slowly and then sliding them into place. Then to repeat the process with my sweatpants, pulling them to my knees as step one, and then, once again keeping the elastic waistband straight and inching it up to my hips before slowly sliding them into place. Although it would seem that these movements are simple things, with my still virtually paralyzed right arm, they were nearly impossible. But it did become much easier when I implemented her suggestions. I just needed to practice a little. We also practiced technique while showering. My concern here was slipping on the wet floor and falling. My OT emphasized using the bars on the wall to transfer into the shower using a "pull to sit" technique. We also put dry towels on the floor which gave me a ton more confidence that I wouldn't slip. Again, these little adjustments seem like simple things, but to me they went a long way toward providing me with the sense of security I needed to feel comfortable. There was no question that the stroke had amplified my reaction to any kind of stress and made me much more paranoid. The other problem I had was dressing myself. I could now handle putting on my sweatpants since my OT's suggestion about focusing on the band and raising and lowering them in stages, but the sweatshirt was a problem since I could barely move my right arm. Then my OT came to the rescue and showed me that if I put my right arm in first and pulled the sleeve up past my right elbow, I could then slip my left arm in the left sleeve, push my head through, adjust the right sleeve now that I had the sweatshirt on and, voila, I was dressed. Once I did it the way she taught me, I never had a problem again. We still had to work on getting my socks and sneakers on and the laces tied, but that was a lesson for tomorrow, and now it was time to do some work. I was still in a wheelchair at that time, so my OT wheeled me into her work area, and we started with a desktop ergometer (an "arms only" machine small enough to rest on a table), which I grasped with both hands and rotated clockwise for 5 minutes and counterclockwise for 5 minutes, to warm up my muscles. Since I was barely able to move the fingers of my right hand, and my grip was very weak we had to strap my right hand to the right handle. Because of that, we spent a fair amount of time on strengthening drills including one that was really proving to be effective, namely twisting and bending into a U-Shape, my Red FlintRehab Resistance Bar, and another where I squeezed her version of a spring-loaded finger/grip strengthener. She didn't ignore my arm and shoulder though and had me do some rotation exercises with another of her devices which was a rod with one end molded into the shape of a hand and the other end covered with rubber. We would place the rubber end on the floor or against the wall and be able to work shoulder rotations at any angle we wanted. I was starting to feel pain in my shoulder now, so we proceeded cautiously. As would be expected, the finger dexterity exercises were the hardest. At that early stage I wasn't even able to pick up coins, such as a penny or dime. I was not even able to touch my index finger and little finger, or thumb and little finger together. To say I was frustrated would be an understatement. My anger was bubbling to the surface again, and I know I showed it. But my OT, who had been through this stage with many patients before me, just let me rant and continued to help me. I quickly gained control, and we finished our session. Good Occupational Therapists definitely have immense patience. Soon it was time for my PT session, and she started me out for 10 minutes on the Elliptical, again having to strap my right hand to the handle and adjust my right leg so it wouldn't fall to the right due to weakness. After I warmed up, we did some exercise to help me with dorsiflexion of my right foot (lifting my toes while the sole of my foot stayed on the floor). I had made no progress so far with this movement. My right foot had remained paralyzed. We tried it with my PT assisting me, and after a few minutes, we saw a slight upward movement of my right toes. I was very excited that more parts of my right side were starting to move and told my PT, "I guess my work is paying off." She told me that I should also concentrate on this movement in my mini gym in my room to hopefully expand the amount of dorsiflex in the foot. We also spent a fair amount of time with me using a walker. With frequent rest stops, my PT and another member of her team escorted me as I walked down a hallway, getting used to the walker. Using it was a welcome relief, because in those first few days, I was able to lean on it as I walked to reduce the body weight my right leg had to support. There was one version of walker that moved forward and sideways that I didn't like because, at that early stage in my recovery, it took too much effort to control its sideward movement. I was also given one that only went straight which I preferred and ended up using exclusively. When I first started using a walker, I had a tendency to hyperextend my right leg, so we all paid close attention to preventing that. We had already noted that my right hamstring (the muscle in the back of my upper leg above my knee) was very weak, which contributed to the hyperextension problem. After lunch that day I was visited by the ST. I told her I was talking to my children that coming evening and would appreciate all the help she could give me to impress them with my improvement from the week before. She helped me work on my articulatory precision by having me over-articulate my words, use a slower rate of talking, and even chuckle, which really worked. She told me my speech was 95% intelligible, that I spoke very clearly as long as I didn't allow fatigue to set in, and that I had learned to exaggerate my words, which helped. She said that I only had a little trouble with advanced words like, "incompetent," and to focus on exaggerating my articulation specifically on those words, even if I spoke slower. She also told me that my swallowing problem was much better, and she was going to recommend an upgrade to a regular diet, thin liquid, and that I start taking my medications whole, still with the applesauce. She still cautioned me to keep practicing all the lessons I had learned on proper chewing and swallowing. This session was another victory for me since everything we practiced could be put to immediate use. And also, another victory for me because tonight I was talking to my children again and I was now less nervous talking to them. They still needed me to reassure them that I wasn't in danger, was already healing, and my rehab was proceeding nicely. It turned out that, when I got on the line that night, only a few days after my last call, the dramatic improvement in my speech, and the easy manner in which I conversed, astounded them. This was my first real indication on how effective the ST sessions were, and it couldn't have come at a better time. There was no doubt in my children's minds anymore, that I was definitely getting better. They all told me that I spoke so well and clearly now that I sounded like an entirely new person from the last call. Another victory for me. Another positive story for Patty to tell me when I started to lose it.

Day Twelve. My OT, PT, and I are already starting to fall into a routine. My OT makes sure that we work hard from 7:00 – 8:00, but she also makes sure I get my breakfast at 8:00 since I need the strength. So, I take a 30-minute breakfast break and then resume at 8:30 with my OT. Then at 9:00 I start with my PT, and a few hours after I finish my session with her, I have my hour with my ST. Once we started today, my OT had me go through a lot of shoulder drills to test my ROM. The drills focused on extending my arm in all directions, and doing a series of rotations. She also had me work on a set of parallel bars where, while standing and holding one bar with my left hand, I extended my right arm and hand, as far as possible without losing my balance, toward another therapist who was placing cones on a table right at the edge of my reach. My job was to remove the cones with my right hand and make a stack of them on the same table. I felt some discomfort in my right shoulder during these drills, as well as in my right knee, but was able to accomplish the task without losing my balance. I also spent time, with my right arm extended and holding a 2' plastic pole in my right hand, of moving the pole horizontally back and forth while my trapezius muscle (muscle between my shoulder and neck) was blocked to prevent it from helping me perform the movement. This exercise was to test my motor control. I had a hard time keeping a grip on the pole due to the weakness of my right hand. When my session started with my PT, once my warmup period was over, we started some coordination drills. A therapist rolled a small yellow ball toward me and had me attempt to kick it back to them with my right foot. It took me a few times to even touch it, but by the 2nd set, I had much more control of my right foot. My kicks also increased in strength as we went into the 2nd set. We also did the modified push-up while lying on my elbows. I did two sets of 10, with a rest period between. My PT also had me on my hands and knees while she was beside me for safety and had me lean forward as much as possible and reach with my left hand, from that position, for the hand of another therapist. It was a good balance test because I was supporting the front of my body with only my weak right arm. I did 10 repetitions of this drill before I ran out of gas. We also worked on leg curls while I'm lying on my stomach, to strengthen the hamstring muscles on the back of my upper leg, which are extraordinarily weak. I am now able to raise my right foot 3" – 4" when we start our sets, but I weaken very quickly. I am just going to have to stay at it, but I admit that it is very frustrating. I've channeled my deep-seated anger enough now that I simply yell at my right leg each day, as if it would actually lister, to start cooperating. That's a better option than me totally losing control. Today the ST brought a mirror, picture cards and asked me several open-ended questions about my goals. She told me to keep looking into the mirror as I answered questions and conversed with her so that I could watch my lip movement as I spoke. She had me once again do my best to pronounce the letters "b, s, f, v, and t." I did much better this time, only having a little trouble with "v and f." In general, though, I had trouble with this entire session because I was so tired from my earlier sessions with my OT and PT. I explained my significant fatigue level to my ST, and she agreed I could not allow fatigue to undermine our sessions. I resolved as the session ended that I was going to try to have my daily schedule adjusted so there would be enough time between PT and ST for me to go to my room and take a nap. I wanted to be fully able to concentrate during my ST sessions, not be half awake. The rest of the day passed uneventfully.

Day Thirteen. When we got to the workout area today, my OT and I worked on weight shift and balance. She had me, from an upright position, shift my weight forward, and then laterally, from side to side. We also used the Parallel Bars. I held on to a single bar and took lateral steps from one end of the bar to the other, and then back to my starting point. Towards the end of the exercise, I had a little trouble with my right knee buckling. My body is still amazingly weak, and I am easily fatigued. Today we also worked on increasing the rotation to the right of my right hand. One of my goals is to play tennis again, and right now, as a result of the stroke, I can't rotate my right hand enough to hold a tennis ball and to toss it into the air as part of my serve. We tried both a one-pound dumbbell and a special wheel which I rolled back and forth on a table (called a supinator/pronator wheel) to increase the rotation of my right hand to the point where a tennis ball rested in the flat of my hand, parallel to the floor. We had little luck during the session, and I had just as little luck when I went back to my room. It's obvious that this is going to take some patience on my part. This was also one of the many times I was thankful that I was left-handed, since I couldn't imagine at that moment, what I would have done if the hand and arm that actually swung the tennis racquet were the ones affected by the stroke. Working my right hand into a position to toss a ball would be easier, by far, than teaching my right shoulder, arm, wrist and hand all the complex motions involved in a tennis swing. When I start my session with my PT, it always begins with a good ten-minute warmup on the Elliptical. After that, for several days now, we have been testing my endurance by walking the hallways with me using a walker and my PT and another therapist along to keep me safe and prevent me from falling. Every day I go a little further, and I become more aware of when I take an incorrect step or drag my right toe as I start a step from my right side. My right toes dragging on the ground is really starting to get to me, but until I get more flexibility in my foot and ankle and until my toes start to move, there isn't much I can do about it. My PT seems happy with my walker-assisted journeys though, because I make it further every day. We concentrated on the walker, the modified pushup, and doing a one-legged squat with my right leg, an exercise we have also been doing for several days. Toward the end of the session, another PT approached us and asked me if I would like to join a group session of recent stroke victims that was being held that evening. For some reason, undoubtedly the stroke's effect on my emotions, being asked that question opened a floodgate of emotions within me and I started to cry. All of my negative feelings about having a stroke came boiling out once again, and it took a few minutes for me to compose myself. I apologized to both PTs, although they both said they understood what I was going through. I agreed to join the group, which were all people who had suffered their stroke within the last few weeks. I realized then that in spite of Patty's stories and my frequent attempts at positive thinking, I still had a lot of resentment in me about suffering a stroke, and I could calm myself all I desired to, but occasionally it would all come to the surface again. My session with my PT was just wrapping up, so she escorted me back to my room to get ready for my next session. When I had my session with the ST, I still was having trouble producing sounds such as "f and v." I found that I was

44

really feeling my fatigue, and it caused me to speak poorly, and not loudly enough to be heard. I admitted to my therapist that I was feeling tired, and it was definitely altering my speech. I re-committed to get my schedule adjusted so this would not happen again. That evening I did participate in the group session. After listening to most of the participants speak, it seemed that some of them were ready to fight as hard as possible to limit the impact of their stroke on their daily lives, while a few others had given in to their plight and resigned themselves to adjusting to the limitations their stroke had placed on them. One particular gentleman spoke of his willingness to fight 24 hours per day to beat his stroke, which was exactly the way I felt. When it was my turn to speak to the group, I repeated almost word for word what he had said, basically that I had declared war on my stroke and would battle as hard as possible to overcome its effects on my life. I spoke with this gentleman after the session and we agreed that the group session was great, but would be even better if someone attended and spoke who was a recovered stroke survivor and could share with new stroke survivors like us, how they had done it, and how they had handled their emotions. We both agreed that for some survivors, hearing from a "vet,", could be the spark they needed to fight back. I crossed paths with the same gentleman several more times at the facility, where we offered each other continued words of support. I also ran into him several times in Outpatient Therapy, once we had been discharged from Inpatient

Therapy, and we again offered each other continued support to keep fighting. By the time we got to Outpatient Therapy, we were both walking unaided, so it seemed like our fighting mentality towards our stroke was paying off.

Day Fourteen. Today my OT had me working on increasing my upper body strength. We used a small, tabletop elliptical for hands only, a small, weighted ball, and a 2-pound dumbbell. We also used the wrist rotation wheel I had used a few sessions ago, although we still had to secure my right hand to it with an Ace bandage. Then we did basic shoulder rotation and extension exercises, to increase my strength and ROM, although they still caused some discomfort in my shoulder. We also used a wall mounted Upper Extremity Rotation Device to further increase my ROM. And, finally, we worked on my wrist strength using the Red FlintRehab Resistance Bar and a 2-pound dumbbell over a small wedge-shaped device lain on a table to support my wrist. We had a breakthrough today. I no longer need the wrap securing my right hand to the Elliptical handle. I could maintain the grip without it. My PT and I noticed that I also was showing increased strength when doing my hamstring (muscles on the back of my thigh) exercises. She then had me, while on my knees with a 2nd therapist behind me to catch me in case I fell, do a series of left to right and forward and back movements to test my balance and ROM. She used a large mirror so I could observe my alignment as I performed these movements. Also, while on my knees, she had me simulate a punching motion, punching with my right hand. I did a set of 10 each in a forward, left and right-side direction. As I progressed through these exercises, the force of my punches increased but my shoulder flex decreased. I did experience some pain in my shoulder. We finished the session with our usual hamstring (muscles on the back of my thigh) curls as well as side leg lifts. When my ST showed up today, she again had the mirror. We did an exercise where she presented me with a picture and asked me to describe it while she recorded me. I was to use the mirror to see my facial expression, since I was also practicing saying certain words slower, and with greater precision. I performed all parts of this exercise without any verbal cues from her. We listened to the audio recordings and noticed that my speech during the exercise was fine, but there was a slight decrease in the clearness of some of the words I spoke, during general conversation. Something else I have to fix.

Day Fifteen. Today, my OT, with a 2nd therapist standing by for my safety, had me stand about 3' away from a raised platform with mat, lean forward to place my hands on the mat, and do 3 sets of modified pushups with standing rest breaks between sets. She then had me, while sitting, work with a wall-mounted Upper Body Rotation Device, to do ROM exercises for my right shoulder. She also had me work the desktop elliptical, which was placed on a higher table to provide a different angle for my shoulder, for two 8-minute segments while standing, with seated rest breaks between segments. I also did an exercise that had me leaning as far forward as my balance would allow, and then extending my reach as much as possible to pick 7 glasses out of a container and then reach out to my maximum ability to another area to stack them. Although a challenge to my balance, I completed this exercise successfully. We also began exercises to simulate me tossing a tennis ball with my right hand. At that moment, I could not rotate my right hand to the right far enough to hold a tennis ball in my palm without it falling to the floor. The purpose of the new exercises was to increase my right-hand rotation to the point that I could hold and toss a real tennis ball on a tennis court as part of my normal serve. During my session with my PT today, she informed me that the strength in my right knee was increasing. Good news. But I can still not do a full hamstring (muscles on the back of my thigh) curl with my right leg, although I am able to raise it a little higher each day. We also did an exercise where, while on my knees, I was given a small plastic racquet to hold in my right hand. My PT would then toss balloons toward me, and I was supposed to bat them back to her using the paddle. The first few balloons I missed completely, until I got my reflexes in order, but after that I managed to return all balloons thrown my way. During my ST session, I was again presented with a mirror to observe my facial and lip movements. Today we did an exercise where I read sentences from a form the ST gave me. I did this exercise with no problem. This was verified when we played back audio of that session. We also recorded me answering open-ended questions and still noted a small reduction in the quality of my speech, and a decrease in vocal strength and endurance. The loss of endurance may be the reason for the lack of clarity in my speech. I am simply getting tired toward the end of the sessions, and it is affecting my speech. I greatly appreciate the audio playback portion of these sessions. They definitely pinpoint the areas that I need to work on. For example, now that I know this, when I have telephone conversations with friends and family, I limit my conversations to about 20 minutes. I'll keep to this routine until the audio feedback shows me that my endurance has increased enough to have longer conversations.

Day Seventeen and Eighteen. I'm strong enough now to use a walker for extended periods. When I go for my weekend walks with a member of the staff, I can cover 2-3 times the distance that I could just a week ago, I'm also able to do longer sessions in my mini gym in my room, where I primarily do exercise band curls for my right arm and right leg, as well as flexibility exercises for my right foot, and rotational exercises for my right ankle. I still can't move my right toes though. I still tire easily and take a nap for about 1 hour each weekend afternoon. I have reached the point with the walker where, although I am escorted to the bathroom by a member of the staff, I can safely transfer myself to the toilet without their assistance, by using the wall-mounted bars. I can also do the same thing as I transfer myself to the seated shower. I can also adjust my pants and underwear by myself, with just my left hand, using my OT's method. In reality I can move about easily, but make sure I keep the trust of the staff by asking for assistance each time I want to move. And, of course, the alarm in the bed and bedside chair would go off if I was foolish enough to try to move without help. At this point I know quite a few of the weekday and weekend staff by their first name and they seem like part of my family. When I buzz for help moving, except at their busiest times, someone is at my door in a matter of seconds.

Day Nineteen. Today my OT evaluated my ability to take a shower by myself, with no help. I passed. She also ensured that I could do all my personal hygiene tasks like brushing my teeth, shaving, and using deodorant, by myself. I passed. And finally, she verified that I could dress myself, including putting on socks and shoes (still can't tie my shoelaces without help). I passed except for the tying shoelaces part. When we went back to the workout area she tested my balance, standing ability, endurance, and the dexterity of my right hand. To do this, she had me do a new exercise in which, while standing, I retrieved yellow and red clothespins from a bin and attached them to a horizontal bar. **Today my PT introduced me to my first**

"Battlefield." She put me on a treadmill, but with immense safety precautions. First, she and another PT strapped me into a harness that was anchored to the ceiling. It strapped snugly around my entire upper body and would keep me from flying off the treadmill if my right leg gave out. Then she and the other PT positioned me on the treadmill so that I could grab two handles while standing erect. One for each hand, to support myself as I walked on the treadmill. Then she started the treadmill, while she and the other PT remained positioned to immediately catch me if I faltered. We started slowly, having me walk, as best I could for 3 minutes. During this time, they taught me how to place my feet, while stepping, on either side of a center line in the tread itself. I immediately found out that I did not have good enough control of my right leg to place it down on the right side of the mid-line with each step I took. Sometimes my right foot would drift to the left, hitting the line or even passing it and landing on the left. We did one 3-minute session at slow speed so I could learn how to do it, and then we did a second and third 3-minute session where my PT gradually turned up the speed of the treadmill. The increased speed immediately showed three major weaknesses in my gait. The first was that my right leg drifted to the left, and my right foot was turned slightly inward with the toes of my right foot pointing to the left. The second thing we learned was that about half the time, my right toes dragged on the treadmill as I was trying to step forward. If I concentrated on stopping the right toes from dragging and made an increased effort to keep it from happening, it happened much less, but, with so many things happening at once, it was hard to maintain that level of concentration. The third thing we learned was that my hip muscles were overwhelming my thigh muscles when I took a step with my right leg and causing the leg to loop out to the right in a kind of half circle when I took a step, instead of my foot moving straight from back to front. We also discovered that all of these things happened more frequently as the speed of the treadmill was turned up to about 2 miles per hour. But the really great news was that I had not only discovered my first Battlefield, a place where I could safely push myself as hard as I was able, but I was walking by myself. Although the harness aided me, it was primarily there for safety. I had to do all the work, and that resulted in me walking. We did three 3-minute sessions, and then I ran out of gas. [*I should mention right here that we used the treadmill only because it was determined that I had enough residual strength left to tolerate it. As mentioned in the Introduction, I worked out hard and often before I had the stroke, and was therefore very fit. Partially due to my fitness level, I was selected for treadmill exercises. I would not have been selected if I did not have this residual strength. The treadmill might be too much for some stroke survivors to handle. Whether it is part of someone's routine will be determined by medical experts. I am simply reviewing how my therapy was managed*]

Overall, I was ecstatic with my 1st Battlefield, the

treadmill. After all, I could push myself to the very edge, and I was walking. Even though there were several things wrong with my gait, I was walking. And this was the point emphasized by my PT. I was walking. Yes, there were some things we had to correct, but the purpose of the treadmill sessions was to evaluate my ability to walk. The fine tuning would happen during future sessions. I had to admit though, as they unstrapped the harness, that although I had gotten the Battlefield I was looking for, I was completely out of gas. The treadmill sessions really pushed me to the edge, as far as my strength and endurance, in my weakened condition. But I was ecstatic, I had just walked on my own without a walker. And, relatively speaking, I had walked really fast. 2 miles per hour in my weakened state felt like 20 miles per hour to me. But I had completed all of the 3-minute sessions, so at least I had enough endurance for that. My PT gave me some time to recover and then we went back to our daily session of hamstring (muscles on the back of my thigh) curls and side and front leg lifts, to continue working to get my right leg stronger. The weakness in the leg was responsible for most of the gait flaws I had just made on the treadmill. That fact motivated me even more to work as hard as possible to strengthen my right leg. It was mostly that single muscle group on the back of my upper right leg that was holding me back. The session was over, so I found my walker and my PT escorted me back to my room. Today, more than any other day, I just lay on the bed and rested as I waited for my ST session, since I was exhausted, and knew how fatigue affected my speech. But, by the time my ST arrived, I was only slightly tired, and ready to go. When we began the ST session today, I was once again tasked with reading prepared sentences, answering questions, and being recorded the whole time. I admitted that I was a little tired, and in the beginning of the session I made a few mistakes, but as we progressed, I grew stronger, and my clarity increased. My overall endurance was building. The ST also evaluated my swallowing, as she had done several times before, and found that it had improved dramatically. I had been eating solid, un-chopped food for several days now, and as long as I prolonged my chewing, I did not have swallowing problems, although I still had an occasional coughing attack, mostly while drinking water.

Day Twenty. Today I have been given a cane to try. Actually, two canes were provided for me to select from. One with a big 4 leg base and one with a smaller 4 leg base. Although you would think the bigger one provides a stronger base, I found the smaller one to be the more versatile choice. Using it requires a bit of time to get the forward swing of it synchronized with my right foot, since I am left-handed, I carry it in my left hand. It also takes a little time to adjust the follow up step with the left foot to be the right length for maximum stability. It definitely doesn't provide the stability of a walker, and it's easier to lose your balance with only it for support, versus the walker which you hold with both hands. I went for multiple test drives with it, with my OT by my side for support. It also takes a while to build your confidence when using it, especially when making turns. But I got the hang of it quickly, so it really wasn't that big of a deal. When we went to the work area today, I worked once again with the Red ClintRehab Resistance Bar, as well as 2- and 3-pound dumbbells to strengthen my elbow and wrist. I also frequently hold a 2-pound dumbbell in my right hand and rotate my hand sharply to the right to teach it to assume that position naturally when I rotate it. We still work daily on these exercises to increase the rotation of my right hand so that I can hold a tennis ball and toss it in the air as though I was really serving the ball, although my number one goal is to play tennis again by the one-year anniversary of my stroke. And in spite of making some progress, I still can't rotate my right hand enough to have it parallel with the floor and be able to cradle the tennis ball in my palm. But diligence will pay off. I am confident, based on my rate of progress, plus the work I do in the mini gym in my room, that I will be able to rotate it to that degree in another few weeks. When I got with my PT today, we started working on heel raises, something I have started to be able to do much better than even a week ago. I stand and hold on to a rail and do sets of 10. Each time I do one, I hold at the top of the raise for a count of 3. When I do them, I also concentrate at the same time on flexing my right hip. The more I can flex it, the better. We also do a version of stretching my hips using steps. I lift my left foot on to the 2nd step and lean into it while allowing my right foot to trail behind and allow my hip and calf to stretch. Today it's back to the Battlefield. I couldn't be happier. I again get suited up for the treadmill. Once more I am fitted with the harness assembly that's attached to the ceiling. And once again my PT and an associate help me onto the treadmill to a point where I can grab the two handles. My PT tells me that today she is going to take the speed of the treadmill a little higher to see how much I can tolerate. We do the first 3-minute set at the speed we were going yesterday, and I concentrate 1st on keeping up and 2nd on keeping each foot on the correct side of the midline on the treadmill track. I still get annoyed because I can hear my toes drag on the track about 50% of the time as I walk faster and faster to keep up with the ever-increasing speed of the treadmill. But I am not bristling with anger. I am just annoyed. Controlling my anger through the strategies I have developed is working. Wait until Patty finds out. She will be so happy. We end the first 3-minute set at a speed of 2 miles per hour, the same speed we finished with yesterday. My PT asks me if I can handle a little more speed during the second 3-minute set and my response is, with a big smile on my face, "bring it." During the second set, she brings the speed up to 2.5 miles per hour, which is as fast as I can go and still keep up the pace while standing erect. I am still, about half the time, looping my right leg as I step due to my hip flexors being out of synch with my thigh muscles. And I am still dragging my right toes.

But, even at the increased speed, I can tell I am doing better than yesterday. I think I have enough fuel in my tank for a third 3-minute set, so we go again, and I was really close to my endurance limit when the end came, and we started slowing down. The treadmill sessions are not for everyone, and I was fortunate that a little of my former conditioning was still there and gave me the strength to go for nine minutes total. It is an amazing exercise though because at 2.5 miles per hour I had to work very hard to keep up with the speed, make sure my feet were aligned, and try to control the looping of my right foot and the dragging of my right toes. Although the hardest exercise I would do while at the facility, it was my favorite. It is my Battlefield. It challenged me in many areas, and I really enjoyed being able to meet that challenge head on. Today when I started my ST session, the ST had me breathe into what's called an incentive Spirometer, which is really just a big tube. I do something similar during my normal annual physical, and based on my effort today, it did not seem that my lung function had been affected by my stroke. We also did an exercise where I repeated a series of fairly long words in one-by-one fashion, making sure I said them slowly and carefully, the way the ST had taught me. When saying the words individually, I achieved 100% accuracy. When saying the words during a conversation, however, my accuracy dropped to 50%. I definitely need to work on talking at a conversational level.

Day Twenty-One. Today we continued my exercises to improve the rotation of my right hand so I can toss a tennis ball into the air from a flat palm. We use a 2 or 3-pound dumbbell to accentuate the right wrist turn to the right, to put my right hand in a palm up position. We're almost there. We also work on my right finger ROM by having me try to expand a small, closed yellow band with just finger strength. We also do an exercise where I bat balloons thrown at me while I hold a small racquet. The difference now is that I am standing and practice maintaining my balance as I hit the balloons. We also continue walking the halls to build my endurance and get more practice with the cane. I have grown used to it now and my gait has adjusted to the proper length to make best use of the cane. I still prefer the walker. We try a new exercise today to help with my right-hand rotation. In this exercise, I rotate my right hand clockwise as far as possible and try to achieve getting my right palm parallel to the floor. Once I get close, I am handed an upside down frisbee to balance in my right hand, without losing control and having it slip from my grasp. At the same time, I have a real tennis racquet that Patty brought from home in my left hand, and I am supposed to simulate a serving motion with my left hand, arm, and shoulder while I balance the frisbee with my right fingers and palm. As I try to simulate the left side serving motion, I am only able to maintain control of the frisbee for a few seconds before my right hand can't hold the extreme rotation to the right and starts rotating back to the left to the degree that I can't prevent the frisbee from falling to the floor. I still have a lot of work to do on the rotation of my right wrist.   My OT also informs me that part of the problem is that I am elevating my right shoulder to try to compensate for my limited elbow and wrist movement, and I must keep my elbow tucked and firmly against my right side to keep my right side aligned properly for the ball toss. I concentrate on keeping my elbow tucked and my shoulder down and see immediate improvement. My OT and I also worked on increasing the mobility of my right fingers by her giving me a very light scarf to hold in my right hand, and to scrunch the scarf into a small ball, just using my right hand and fingers. Once I finished scrunching it into a small ball, I was to toss it in the air, catch it with my right hand, and repeat the process. This exercise was much harder than I first thought, and I spent many minutes before I could repeatedly manipulate the scarf into a small ball, toss it up into the air, and then do the whole thing again. I really liked this exercise as it really helped with my right finger dexterity, and my tossing motion, and said so to my OT, who promptly gave me one to take back to my room and add to my little mini-gym routine. In retrospect, this one exercise accelerated to a great degree the return of my finger dexterity. I noticed a huge improvement in just a few days after I added 10 minutes of scarf manipulation to my daily routine in my room. My OT added one final exercise for me. This consisted of sitting on a raised table and turning my trunk so I could grab beanbags out of a container at my side, which I had to turn my body to access. This trunk rotation doesn't seem like much, but every exercise I do to loosen my right side and increase my balance and flexibility puts me a few more days ahead of schedule to meet my number one short-term goal, which is to walk unaided. Today with my PT we started the next phase of the plan to get me walking. We started having me walk backward. We practiced with me holding on to a parallel bar. My PT stressed that I do the hip and knee movements in exaggerated fashion, then the properly-timed hip movement, and finally, the properly-timed foot placement. All these things have to be done correctly to give me the proper foot clearance to step backwards. We practiced each movement separately, and it was much harder than I thought. I remember thinking to myself at that moment, "I really do have to learn to walk all over again. It's like I'm starting with a new leg that doesn't know how to do anything." But I managed to put the pieces together and slowly walked backward while firmly grasping the parallel bar. Today we also started to get me stepping side to side on a 15' long stepping mat on the floor. My PT had me sidestep first left, then right, 3 full lengths of the floor mat. It was very difficult for me since I still had trouble raising my right foot more than a few inches. The 3rd thing my PT started me doing was practicing a step up/step down exercise on the portable stairs unit they had there. She had me do 2 sets of 15, using the first step which was 6" off the floor. We were definitely stepping up our floor work with the backward and side-to-side exercises, which I found amazingly difficult for the first few days. It was mainly a lack of confidence on my part, oriented around the remaining small challenge to my balance, which is a huge part of these exercises. Once I worked the step up/step down on the stairs for a few more days, strengthening my right leg lifting ability since I had to lift my body 6" with my bad leg 15 times in succession, it became easier to perform both of these other movements. Slowly but surely, I was practicing all of the movements associated with learning to walk again. When it was time for my ST today, we spent most of the time assessing how I was doing. First, the ST had me perform various speech patterns looking for my level of competence. She used a Voice Analyst application on her laptop to record me and show me right on the screen that I was doing well. She also observed me as I stated 16 specific words and had me tap my finger while speaking when I hit a natural break within the word. An example would be the word, "shoeshine." She also observed whether I paused between words during a conversation with her, to monitor whether I left enough space between words. She indicated I was progressing well, and I was maintaining a success rate of over 80% during these drills. She also said I was doing just as well with 10-12 letter words during our conversation. We did another exercise where I went through 10 separate series where I had to converse with her using what I had been taught about exaggerating longer words, while she evaluated me. At the end of this exercise, I was basically told that for those particular exercises, I was speaking error-free, so, I guess I got a 100%. We did one more of the same type of exercise with even longer words, after which I was told I was still speaking correctly over 80% of the time.

Day Twenty-Two. Today my OT started me out using the wall-mounted Upper Body Rotation device, while standing, to flex, extend, and rotate my right arm and shoulder. The purpose of these exercises was to strengthen the shoulder and improve its functional use, especially to better help me rotate my right hand and wrist. We also did a series of exercises where I squeezed my shoulder blades together to also strengthen the shoulder and increase its functional use. We also continued my hallway walks, going further and further each day as my overall strength and balance continued to improve. It was on this date that I started to visualize myself walking unaided. Walking without aid by my discharge date was still a short-term goal I was determined to achieve. **Today marks the day when I first get to do battle on my second Battlefield**. By now I had progressed to the point with all the right leg exercising where I could take a short step to my left or right without losing my balance. So, I had asked my OT if I could have Patty bring in one of my real tennis racquets and a bag of balls, and have one of her associates toss a ball a tiny bit to my left or right while I simulated a position as if waiting to receive a serve, and then with my OT as well as one of her associates ready to catch me if I stumbled or lost my balance and started to fall, I would hit the tossed ball, either by stepping into a forehand, or a backhand return. She agreed to let me try it as long as we took the proper safety precautions, so today was the big day. This was another case where I was fortunate that I was left-handed, since I swung the racket normally using my left hand, versus my weakened right. We set up with an OT standing directly in front of me, about 15 -20 feet away, and she started throwing tennis balls at me, trying to get them to bounce a little to my left or right and allowing me to take a short step in either direction and hit a forehand or backhand return. It took us a few tries to get coordinated, but soon I was stepping left and right, swinging the racquet, and hitting the ball in my normal rhythmic fashion. I cannot begin to express the joy I felt doing this simple little drill, which was just a small confirmation that perhaps the promise I had made to myself about really playing tennis on the anniversary date of my stroke was soon to be within reach. We did this exercise for about 15 minutes, at which point I started to get fairly tired, and we took a break. There was no question as the session progressed, that this was my 2nd Battlefield. Here I could push myself as hard as I possibly could. And although I really wanted to hit tennis balls, this activity definitely helped me channel my aggression into my swing, take steps forward as well as sideways and improve my overall balance and stability. I was extremely grateful to my OT for making this happen and thanked her profusely. This, to me, was just another example of the staff of the rehab facility going the extra mile to help a patient. To make today's session complete, we then went to the general workout area and worked with free weights, the tabletop wrist rotation wheel, and the Red ClintRehab Resistance Bar exercises to continue to work on increasing my rotation of my right hand to get the open palm of my hand parallel with the floor. I am getting close. I have about 1" more of wrist rotation to go to hit my goal.   Today we took the plastic support off my right foot. Time to start walking with both tennis shoes on. I immediately noticed my right toe catching on the floor some of the time with the AFO removed. Time to concentrate on lifting the right foot higher when I take a step. We then went back to Battlefield #2, the treadmill, and my PT and her associate strapped me into the harness assembly. As usual, we went through the normal speed increase between 3-minute sets, but this time we held a steady 2.5 miles per hour for the third set. I was going at that speed without the plastic support on my right ankle, and I felt a significant increase in toe drag, and a small amount of an outside loop in my right leg gait by the 3rd set. I felt for some reason that my right leg somehow had gotten weaker, and negatively affected my performance. I mentioned my disappointment to my PT, and she reminded me that this was the first day on the treadmill without the ankle device for support, and that for me to take that into consideration. Her reminding me of the absence made me feel better. Sometimes I can get overcritical of my performance without thinking it through. I admitted to myself that it would take me more time to function correctly without the ankle device, and cleared my mind of negative thoughts. It was right then that I realized that my anger was under control, I was thinking rationally about something which would have made me angry a week ago. My Battlefield and Think Happy Thoughts concepts really were working. I still believe that the treadmill, as long as I'm wearing the support harness, and have my PT and her partner standing by for my safety, is the toughest machine to master. But the most rewarding. I also believe the treadmill is an awesome device to help speed recovery and build endurance. During our session today, I was also introduced to a new walker that, according to my PT, will help normalize my stride and improve the cadence associated with my gait. I just have to get used to setting the brakes each time I park to go to another activity. We did several new tests during my ST session today. First, I was tasked with inhaling as deeply as possible and then counting out loud, from 1 – 20 using that single breath. I was able to do this without difficulty. Second, I was tasked to inhale and then prolong certain vowel sounds by voicing the sound for as long as I could while exhaling. I was able to achieve this test for 17 seconds, which was in the middle of the expected range. Third I was tasked with saying certain letters such as "p, t, and k" as fast as I could while my rate of saying them was tracked by my ST. This test evaluated the correct function of my jaw, lips and tongue. I was also tested for proper words being spoken when my nose was involved in my speech. And I was monitored to see if I displayed the proper amount of rhythm when speaking during a normal conversation. I was within normal limits on all these tests, so all our work was paying off. All of these tests were an example of how thorough and professional the STs were as they worked to help me improve my speech. I was impressed with them all.

Day Twenty-Three. Today we once again did the exercise where an OT stood 15 – 20 feet in front of me and tossed tennis ball to my left and right sides, forcing me to take a single step to my left or right to hit a forehand or backhand return. In just the time since we did this exercise yesterday, I could tell that I had much better balance when moving laterally and even ahead at an angle. Today I managed to not only hit the ball with authority, but, close to 90% of the time, hit close to a target I was aiming at. Yesterday we had performed this exercise outside, while today we did it inside. This allowed me to identify a specific target to aim all my returns at. We did this exercise for 10 – 15 minutes, and my left and right body rotation, my left and right reaching ability, and right to left weight shifting ability improved by the minute. In addition, this was a great exercise to build my endurance and get a good cardio workout in general. When we finished, I was happy and felt renewed motivation to work my tail off on the strengthening drills for my right leg. My OT's ability to tailor my workout to allow me this favor was not only generous of her, but turned out to significantly improve my lateral movement as well. I never ceased to be amazed at how she and the other OTs showed their willingness to do new things to help me on the road to recovery. We continued to work on my stepping ability with an exercise where I was given a 2-pound weighted dowel and tasked with using it to hit a small ball thrown by one of my OT's colleagues. This exercise was easier than I expected due to my hand/eye coordination being improved by the tennis ball drill. We also continued to walk the hallways with my new walker to build my leg strength, and general strength, since this new walker took more effort to control. I saw the wisdom of making the switch however, since I could work on my gait as well as my balance and control with this walker versus the walker I had before, which rolled in a straight line automatically and did not require the "driver" to control it. When I started today with my PT, she told me my overall gait was improving each day except for the continued toe drag, which I am focusing on improving without the benefit of having the plastic ankle support. I do feel, and my PT agrees, that the frequency of the toe drag is less as I consciously focus on lifting my right foot higher each time, I take a step. I'm beginning to see that for this particular problem, namely the toe drags, it will simply be a case of constant repetition of doing it correctly, to teach my brain to do it automatically. I will focus on properly lifting my right foot for as long as it takes. I am committed to reaching the day when I have finally taught my right foot to lift itself to the proper height automatically. Whatever it takes. Today, once again I am going to battle. We are going to use the harness affixed to the ceiling and the treadmill. We went through our normal three sets of 3 minutes each without incident. Today my PT wanted to do interval training where she would vary the treadmill speed from slower to faster and raise the treadmill angle at the same time, basically increasing the difficulty in two ways, speed and incline. My job was to maintain my posture through these changes. I voiced a slight concern about hyperextending my right knee while doing this, but we tried an abbreviated version first, and I could see for myself that a hyperextension was not going to occur, so we moved ahead with the actual drill. Once we started, my PT would increase speed and incline for 10- 15 seconds and then return to the original slower, flat position. My job was to maintain the correct upright posture and focus on the proper lifting of my right foot to eliminate the intermittent toe drag. This was where the true Battle started in my mind as I challenged myself to attack the new positions as hard as I could, and exceed each new increment. And, I did exceed them. What a feeling. When we were finished with the treadmill, I felt that my foot alignment when stepping was improved by this drill and definitely improved from when we first started using the treadmill. Today, after the treadmill, we started a new exercise which was really vital to recovery in a completely different way. My PT had me lay flat on a padded mat that was placed on the floor, and then, without assistance and without grabbing anything to assist me, I had to find a way to get to my feet. The idea here was that at some point I very well might fall, and I needed to know how to get back to my feet, unaided in any way. It seemed intimidating when this latest task was first presented to me, but after a little experimenting, I found that if I placed both hands on the mat, and got both feet under me, that even with my weakened right side, I was able, without problem, to use my legs to raise myself to a standing position. And I found that as many times as I was asked to repeat the process from a position of lying totally flat on the floor, getting to my hands and feet and then using my legs to raise myself up to a standing position worked every time, and was quite safe. There was no question that all the strengthening work on both my arm and leg were definitely making me stronger. Even two weeks ago I would not have had the strength on my right side to accomplish what I was accomplishing now. During ST today we worked some of the same drills that we did yesterday and used the same Voice Analyst app on her laptop as before. It seemed, when we were done that my percentages were better. Today, my speech was clear over 90% of the time. When I was asked to spontaneously respond to a list of questions the therapist asked me, I was very close to 90% clear, and when I performed an exercise where I selected a category of difficult words, and then spoke each one, I was again over 90% intelligible. In fact, on the last drill, I was close to 100%.

Day Twenty-Four and Twenty-Five. On Saturday when I get up, while I'm eating my breakfast, I starting thinking about leaving this place that has become like home to me. It suddenly comes rushing into my head, "if what my PT told me earlier in the month is still true, next Saturday I'll be walking out of here. But I'm not ready. There's no way I could do it right now, I can barely shuffle sideways, or backwards without losing my balance. If the rail wasn't there to hold on to, I'm sure I would lose it. But then I think, "my PT's a professional, she'll know if I'm ready or not. Don't worry about it." So, I don't. I block those thoughts out and start working my foot exercises. I'm going to get my toes moving if it's the last thing I ever do. A little while later, Patty walks in. In spite of my attempt to block out my thoughts about leaving, I tell her about them. As I tell her, we both decide to do a comparison between the "me" that sits here right now, and the "me" that came here 17 days ago. It doesn't take long, as we begin to compare, before we become amazed at the changes that have occurred. The Day 7 "me" could barely move. Today's "me" has enough strength to wander the hallways for hours with his new walker if he nagged the weekend shift to give him that much time, and is starting to walk backwards and also sideways. The Day 7 "me" had a hard time talking, could barely eat, even though his food was chopped, could not take his medications unless they were crushed and mixed with applesauce, and had a hard time taking even a tiny sip of water. Today's "me" can chatter on for hours, eats

70

whole, un-chopped food, takes his whole tablet medications 2 or 3 at a time with water versus applesauce, and drinks many different liquids, including his morning coffee, with only an occasional cough. The Day 7 "me" couldn't go to the bathroom, shower, or groom himself without assistance. Today's 'me" can do all of those things by himself. The Day 7 "me" couldn't dress himself or tie his shoes. Today's "me" can do all that without assistance. The Day 7 "me" wouldn't have dreamt of stepping into forehands and backhands with a real tennis racquet and ball. Today's "me" has already done it – twice. The Day 7 "me" sure couldn't have moved at over 2 miles per hour on a treadmill for 9 minutes. Today's me has also already done that – 3 times. We stop right then and just sit in awe as we review what has happened to me in just 17 days without us really putting it all in perspective. I think about the amazing job my OT, PT, and ST have done and wonder, "where would I be without them?" then Patty says, "this is how you've changed in just over two weeks. You've still got another week to go. If your PT said you'll walk, I think she knows what she is talking about. I think you will walk." The little exercise we just finished has convinced me to stop thinking about next weekend and to go back to work. So that's what I do. For the rest of the weekend, I work at my mini gym workstations, especially the one I have rigged up for my foot. On Sunday afternoon I have another breakthrough. My right big toe is moving! The remaining toes look like they move too. Just the tiniest little bit, but they seem to be moving. But, the big one for sure. This is awesome, because the lack of toe movement is the main thing messing up my gait. If I can get them to raise when I step, I can eliminate that frustrating toe drag. This is the best weekend yet. All my joints are moving now, and other than the pain in my shoulder, I feel really good. I can hardly wait to start working again tomorrow.

Day Twenty-Six. Today we are going to work on my functional reach while standing. In other words, how far can I push my reach and corresponding weight shift with just my two feet for support? It turns out that my little Battlefield #2 tennis exercise is a great test of that, so we set up to do it again. I have my racquet, and in the same room as last time, an OT standing 15 – 20 feet away tosses a tennis ball to either my left or right, far enough away from me that I have to take a lateral step, either left or right, to hit the ball, and I have to reach as I extend my arm to actually swing the racquet properly. Taking the left or right step is becoming easier each day, as is my reach to catch the ball with my arm fully extended. In fact, as long as I remember to lead with my bad right foot first, I can now do 2 steps. But, when I forget and lead with my left, I always stumble when stepping to my left. But I don't get angry like I did just a week ago. I'm really starting to get past the pity party stage now that I have my two Battlefields. Also, since we have now done this drill multiple times, I wonder to myself if my increased right foot mobility is due to my right toes finally starting to move. Definitely a possibility. We have some fun today. As the balls are tossed to me, I just hit them back to the young man tossing them to me without too much pace to see if he can catch them. So, in essence, he becomes the target. When we finished with the tennis exercise, we did another new one. In this latest exercise, I wear a Velcro mitt on my right hand, with the hand rotated to the right as far as possible, and try to catch a Velcro ball as it is tossed to me. I only had moderate luck with this exercise as the ball bounced off the mitt on many occasions rather than sticking to it as was supposed to happen. These misses were mainly my fault as I still have trouble maintaining a palm up position with my right hand. After this, we went back to the wall-mounted Upper Body Rotation device and I did a series of shoulder rotation exercises to continue improving my strength and the functional use of the shoulder. I still have pain in my shoulder when we rotate it in certain directions. We also worked on my wrist with the Green FlintRehab Resistance Bar. I had made enough improvement in my wrist strength and grip strength that I was able to move up to the more difficult Green Bar. I also worked with a 3-pound dumbbell. My wrist rested on the same small support I'd used in the past to do my wrist curls and work on my wrist strength. When my session started with my PT, I did 10 minutes as usual on the Elliptical machine and then it was back to Battlefield #1, the treadmill. It looks like we are really testing my limits today because my PT informed me that we are going to do 5 sets, versus the 3 sets I was accustomed to. I thought right then, "if I'm going to be walking unaided by the end of the week, this is a good way to get me ready." Every time we've done this exercise, I've noticed that there are two sets of handles on the machine and that, as the sessions increased, I am better able to maintain my upright posture and generally walk straighter, by holding the set of handles furthest from me. Holding this set has helped me keep my arms straighter. I mentioned this to my PT and she had the other set of handles removed to make the 2nd set easier to access. What a difference that makes. I feel more comfortable, right from the start. It turned out we are doing our first three 3-minute sets at 2.0 miles per hour, and the last two at 2.5 miles per hour. I make it through all 5 sets, and I'm pretty sure that my toe drag was less. I credit the new handle placement and my ability to raise my toes a little as the reasons. My PT also told me that I was displaying more toe slap which means I am doing more of a heel-to-toe step, which is good. She also says that my gait was lengthening, which is also good. I also believe it is because I feel stronger on my right side than ever before. But, whatever the reason, it's all good. I'm getting close to walking unaided. We then went back to the exercise where I laid on a mat on the floor and had to get to my feet. As last time, putting 2 hands down first and then getting to both feet and using my legs to push my body upward did the trick. I must admit, though, that the last few times I did this I was starting to get tired, and it showed.

We then did my daily hamstring (muscles on the back of my thigh) curls. I remember my frustration when I could not seem to get stronger in this exercise. I still could raise my leg, but only about an inch further than last week. I remember voicing my frustration to my PT, who told me the same thing as the last time I complained, "be patient." To take my mind off my leg problem she took me for my daily walker-aided walk in the hallways. I was able to go whatever distance she mapped out without any fatigue at this point. I was totally comfortable with this walker, and it was very useful when practicing the proper gait. The longer walks were also helping me build my endurance, and I was definitely sleeping better at night. We tried another new exercise during my ST session today. I swear, the ST group thinks of everything. Today, the ST had me use my cell phone to call hers and have a general conversation about my weekend and about how I felt our therapy was progressing so far. The call was complete with turning on some music to create a little background noise so I would have to speak more forcefully. It was a great exercise, because it was something I would be doing daily in the future. We talked for 10 – 15 minutes and my ST monitored everything. During the conversation there were a handful of spots where I had to slow down and more thoroughly pronounce, or repeat a word I had just spoken too quickly, but overall, I did well. I now feel comfortable talking to anyone. In fact, I was in daily conversation with my company since we were at a point where they needed my input, and during those conversations, as long as I concentrated on speaking slowly, and didn't talk for hours, my employees seemed able to understand every word I spoke. I also received input from co-workers that I didn't sound like someone who had experienced a stroke, especially just a month ago. Another victory for me.

Day Twenty-Seven. My OT had us set up for our tennis exercise again today, so back to Battlefield #2. Working in both Battlefields is so therapeutic. I get to push myself to the limit in both and in this one I get to hit stuff. It may sound trivial, but once I declared war on my stroke and I could do a little self-hypnosis to convince myself that I was really physically fighting my stroke, good things have started to happen. I have been steadily improving going left or right to take the one or two lateral steps I need to hit the ball. I've also gotten more confident in increasing the speed and length of the step itself. There are no balance issues. I feel it is evident since I range further to each side each day. I totally believe that my renewed state of mind is responsible for my sudden improvement. And, it hasn't gone unnoticed. Both my OT and PT have commented on my physical improvement and have told me that I am really starting to take off. That's important to me, but they have both also commented that I seem happier. I've told them both the decision I made about going to war, and my two Battlefields. Since they knew me pretty well at this point, each one laughed when I told them and said, "that sounds like you." They both also said one other thing, even though I told them at different times and places. They said to me, "recovering from something this serious IS a battle, and different people fight it in different ways. The bottom line is whatever works for you. A big part of the battle is in your mind. The harder you fight and use that brain of yours, the quicker you will recover. You keep doing what you're doing." We did my tennis drill for about 15 minutes, and then went back to the normal workout room for some fine motor control exercises. When we got to the workout room, my OT had me begin a new exercise called a Ring Tree. This was a coordination drill where I had to retrieve round washers of various inside diameters from a bin at my side that contained 10 or more, and then place them on the same sized dowel on a rack in front of me. This sounds easy, but the drill is, in essence, multi-leveled since I had to reach to the side at one level, then to place dowels at different levels, and different diameters, all with my troublesome right hand which still tended to wander. I did the drill, but it took great focus to maneuver my weak arm to the right dowel and the right level. I also did a 2nd exercise where I had to reach to my maximum and unstack a stack of plastic cups and make a new stack, without allowing any cup to touch the table they were on as I restacked them. Again, it sounds easy, but fully extending my weak arm, which tended to wander, and keeping it from wandering into contact with the table took quite a bit of concentration. In the end, though, I was able to accomplish this seemingly easy task. By now I was getting tired, so I struggled a little when my OT had me do an exercise where I simply had to grab a cup of water from the table, bring it to my mouth, and take a sip. I did it, but grasping the cup with my right hand, which I still had trouble with as far as grip strength, proved to be harder than it should have been. We did one final exercise where we simply tossed a 2-pound medicine ball back and forth from a distance of about 3 feet. This one didn't prove to be too difficult, and I completed it with no problem. When I met with my PT today, we right away went for a long stroll with my walker. I probably did the best so far as far as maintaining a proper gait. My toe drag is happening less and less, probably because I am walking further each day with the walker and my strength continues to build. I also rarely hyperextend my knee on our walks now, but I think that is more because I nearly always bend the right knee as I step, to try to simulate the movement of my left leg. When we finished our walk, it was back to Battlefield #1. Today we did four 3-minute segments. The first two at 2.5 miles per hour and the last two at 2.3 miles per hour. Even though the overall speed was faster, I seldom felt the toe drag, and my stride is continuing to get better. There is no question in my mind that I have gained significant overall strength in my right leg as a result of our treadmill sessions. The long walks with the walker are definitely helping too. Today my ST had me do some new exercises. She had me read 15-word sentences while she listened for appropriate volume and clarity. Although she told me that overall, my accuracy was over 90%, I missed a word on occasion and took a little time to correct my speech when I felt I had to correct something I said that wasn't clear. She also told me that my breathing was good, which means my ability to breath correctly while reading, or just having a casual conversation is fine.

Day Twenty-Eight. This morning we had a breakthrough. I put on my own tennis shoes and tied the laces, without any assistance. It's a small thing, but a huge victory for me. I had tried every morning for 2 weeks to tie my shoelaces, and even managed to do it once in a while, but most of the time my right-hand finger dexterity just wasn't there. Today it was. All that time doing the scarf exercise was paying off. After celebrating with my OT, we go straight to Battlefield #2 and set up our quick step tennis drill in which a therapist tosses tennis balls to my left and right from 15 – 20 feet away, and I take one or two lateral steps to the left or right and hit either a forehand or backhand return to the person throwing the ball. This exercise helps to improve my balance, weight shift both forward' backward, and bi-laterally, timing, and eye-hand coordination. We did this exercise for 15 – 20 minutes. We then went to the workout area and my OT had me do a new exercise. In this new exercise, cones are placed a few feet apart with a very light plastic bar connecting them. The purpose of the exercise is to step over the bar, which can be adjusted to different heights.

The real-life comparison to this exercise would be stepping over a shower threshold. We started with the connecting bar set 2.5" above the ground, and I, while holding on to a parallel bar for overall support, stepped over the bar 6 times. The bar was then raised to 5", and I stepped over it 8 times. I stepped over the bar in a forward direction and also a lateral direction. This is a perfect exercise for me since we have a 5" sunken living room at home which I will have to navigate once I am released. We then did another finger flexibility exercise during which I, using my right hand only, retrieved 20 pegs from a basin and placed them in a pegboard to increase my "pinch and grasp/release capability. We then did another exercise where I had to pick up twenty 1" wooden blocks and put them in a basin. We did 3 sets of twenty. We also did a full set of forward and lateral shoulder rotations while I was standing. My PT and I went for another long walk this morning, with me using the walker. She is definitely evaluating my gait as we do it. When we returned, she got me suited up for Battlefield #1 one more time. We did four 3-minute segments today with the speed steadily increasing from 2.0 miles per hour to 2.5. I still experience some toe drag and swinging or my right leg, but it is much less than when we started. And, we are going faster. I am definitely stronger on my right side than I was a week ago. After the treadmill, we returned to what is called the agility ladder, a mat on the floor that resembles a ladder. My PT had me walk sideways across the length of the ladder. When I was about to begin, I was supporting myself by leaning on a counter prior to taking my first step. It took me a while to start, I was a little afraid to lose the counter's support. I finally did 3 sets on the 15' ladder, and then I did 4 sets of backwards steps. I had some trouble in each portion of the exercise with correctly placing my right foot in the space in front of, or behind me during this exercise. My foot still wanders a bit when we are moving laterally or backward. When it was time for ST, we started with a 10-minute period where I spoke while being recorded. I should note here that our sessions are only ½ an hour long, and have been that length for a few days. My assumption is that I have progressed to the point where that's enough time to implement their remaining agenda. When we played back my conversation, I noticed a few short sections where I sped up my rate of speaking, but there were few, and I quickly corrected those. Overall, I was close to 100% accurate. I do remember commenting on the overall recording by saying, "I want to be perfect, that one could have sounded better." The ST also made the suggestion that I use my breathing as a pacing marker. I will start paying even more attention to my breathing.

Day Twenty-Nine. Today, as usual my OT started me on the desktop elliptical, with me turning the wheels in each direction for 7 minutes. then I first laid on my back and did some chest presses using 4 - 6-pound weights, and then stood and did standard bicep curls using the same weight range. Then she took me for a long walk still using my walker, before turning me over to my PT. Today, after warmup, we went back to the cone test. This time, however, I was told to step backward over the attached bars, which were set 5" from the floor. I had trouble with this one and was only able to successfully clear the bar about 50% of the time. My PT offered to lower the bar for me, but I declined. I was determined to force my right leg to become strong enough that I could clear the bar 100% of the time. My PT now informs me that today is the day. I am going to walk unaided. I'm ready. This is what all this work has been for. My PT and her helper put me in a wheelchair and wheeled me down to a side entrance. They parked outside the doors and then, with one of them on each side of me, I started walking across the parking lot. If, in the future anyone tells me that parking lots are flat, they really need to take a closer look. There were subtle 1" waves across the pavement that gave me fits. Each one seemed more like 1' than 1". But, by shortening my step length, and focusing on keeping my right foot straight, I was able to negotiate them. I was going at turtle speed, but without assistance, and I was happy. Then my PT pointed me toward the sidewalk, which had a fairly steep uphill incline. I thought to myself when I saw that, "No way can I do that." But I was wrong. I made it up the sidewalk without any help. Then my PT pointed to the right, and there was another sidewalk. This one had a significant downhill incline. So off we went, and, although I took really small steps and kept my knees bent to keep my balance, we made it to the bottom. At the bottom, my PT had me step from the sidewalk to the street, and back to the sidewalk, using the methods she had taught me. Again, I was able to accomplish those steps. Then we headed back up the sidewalk. At the top we kept right on going, and in another few seconds I was walking on gravel. I walked about 40' on the gravel and had a few incidents where my balance was off a little and I was forced to self-correct. I also had one incident where my guardian angels had to catch me and help me regain my balance when I stepped into a small depression. We finally made it back to the sidewalk and headed down to the parking lot and my parked wheelchair. I made that walk unassisted and we finally got back to my wheelchair. I did it. I walked unassisted, and although I had to stop twice to get my balance with my guardian angels steadying me, I didn't fall. I got congratulations from them both, and then we headed back to the workout room. I was extremely proud of myself, but also realized how far I still had to go to walk with confidence. When we got back to the workout room, we headed for the mock stairs. First my PT had me hold a rail for safety and ascend and then descend three 4" steps and then two 6" steps, to work on my right foot and toe alignment. Then we did some balance and right-hand rotation testing. My PT had me hold a foam tray with 5 upsides down glasses on it, like a waiter would, balanced on the tips of the fingers of my right hand, and walk a distance of about 40 feet. I did this task but then she turned the glasses right side up and had me do it again. This time, making two 40' walks, I dropped 4 - 5 glasses each time due to the smaller base diameter. Then she filled one of the glasses about ¾ full of water and had me carry that on the tray, again with my right hand as a waiter would, during one of my 40' walks. I was starting to lose the ability to hold the amount of wrist turn to balance the tray, and had 7 spills during my walk as the tray tilted due to my weakened right hand. When I had finished this walk, I went to the area of each spill and wiped it up as I squatted to reach the spots on the floor. The squatting did not bother me. We wrapped up the session with me doing more squats to test the strength of my right leg after the morning's activity. I only had to squat 3 more times. Today when I met the ST, she had me read passage she had brought with her. She had me read it two times in a row to test my pacing, breathing, and whether I paused at the right moment to breath and avoid vocal fatigue. Other than feeling a little fatigue, I felt that I repeated the passage very well. My ST agreed with me. I also dictated some phrases into her iPad so she could objectively assess how clearly I spoke. I got a score of 50 out of 51 or 98% on the dictation test. I definitely have benefited from all the ST's hard work. I feel at this time that I can now talk to anyone for an extended period of time without becoming hard to understand.

Day Thirty. Today is, if I pass the final tests of all 3 therapy groups, my last day of working with these amazing people. I've already had my M.D. evaluation, and I passed. So, the three therapy groups are left. For sure they have helped me get to a point that a month ago I wouldn't have thought possible. My OT is going to do her evaluations first. The first evaluation is to determine whether I can go to the bathroom without assistance. I wheel my walker to a spot next to the toilet and, using the wall handles, correctly transition to the toilet without problem. I demonstrate how to remove my cloths safely so I can go, simulate going, and then redress safely. Finally, I correctly transition back to my walker. All done the right way. I pass. The second of her evaluations is to determine if I can safely shower. So. I'm going to take one right now with her observing. I must do everything the way she taught me. That includes transferring from the walker into the shower space the way she taught me, by using the handles on the wall, which I do. Then I shower, while seated, again following the way she taught me, always using the wall handles and not leaning off the seat past the point of good balance. I do these things too. Now I dry myself and then transfer back to the walker the way she taught. I'm fine with that too. So, I ace that evaluation. It's vital for me to do all of this right because I will do it every day at home. We have already converted the bath at home in our master bedroom to be set up very similarly to the bathroom here, with a seat, multiple wall handles, and a no slip floor mat. Next, I use the walker to go to the sink and go through my normal daily hygiene, keeping the walker parked the way I was taught. So, I shave, brush my teeth, etc. with no problem. I pass. Now it's time for the next evaluation. Can I dress myself? I wheel my walker to the main room and transition to the chair. My clothes and shoes are already laid out, so I proceed to dress myself following the way she taught me, including putting on and lacing my shoes. I do it all correctly, so I pass that one too. So, the first four are done. The fifth one is, do I eat correctly? Breakfast has arrived so I go through the process of eating. Swallowing is not a problem for me any longer and I eat whole, un-chopped food, so I consume the meal with no problem. I pass that evaluation too. Now it's time to go to the workout area. She does a final test on my progress of rotating my right wrist far enough that I can hold a Frisbee and move my left arm as though playing tennis. I can now do this test and maintain my control over the frisbee. We also try the tennis ball toss, and I can now rotate my right hand far enough to toss the ball as though I was in a real game. Mission accomplished. We also go for a short walk with me using my walker so she can observe my upper body control. I have no problem. I am much stronger that when I was admitted. My OT has now finished with her evaluations. I passed them all. One down. Next, I go spend time with my PT. It turns out my evaluation is another go at "walking the parking lot." This is basically music to my ears, because I now know what to expect. Yesterday, my steps were extremely tentative, made with a combination of caution and fear of the unknown. Today I will do better. The parking lot is now known to me. My PT and her partner again wheel me down to the side entrance and we park outside. I feel more confident already because we walked this area yesterday. As before we start walking the parking lot. My stride, although I am still very cautious, is longer today. The small ripples in the parking lot don't bother me today either. I just slightly exaggerate the height of my right foot when I step and glide right over them. Also, I feel more confidence when walking up and then down the sidewalk. Yesterday I seriously shortened my steps, but today I try to keep a normal stride and simply adjust my posture forward or backward to keep my balance. I like this approach better. We then practice stepping down to the street and back up to the sidewalk, like we did yesterday. I can do these steps easily. We then follow the sidewalk up to the gravel covered area we walked yesterday and walk the gravel again. I am keeping the same stride length here as when I started today, and even on the gravel it is no problem. My PT then throws a slight curveball my way by directing me to walk a grassy area with notable uneven patches. I walk this cautiously, but try to hold the same stride. It's really no problem as long as I concentrate on lifting my right foot. My PT has emphasized during the entire walk for me to keep my eyes up when walking, which I'm sure is part of the evaluation. Yesterday when we made this walk, I was constantly looking at my feet. Today, I do as she asks, and kept my eyes up. It makes little difference as long as I raise my right foot. We continue through the grass and make it back to the sidewalk leading down to the side entrance. Again, I have no trouble with the slightly steep downward grade as long as I adjust my posture by leaning back slightly. We make it back to the wheelchair without incident. I am extremely happy because I have completed the walk with my eyes up, with a much longer stride than yesterday, and without requiring any help from falling from my PT or her partner. I also feel strong, with gas still in my tank. It looks like my PT was right. Figuratively speaking, I will walk out of here tomorrow. Even though facility policy will require me to be in a wheelchair, I know I could walk, although slowly and cautiously, if for some reason I had to. When it comes time for my ST evaluation, I get a visit from the boss of that department. That was my first surprise. She and I had a general conversation for about 15 minutes and then the conversation switched to music. During one of my earlier sessions, I had told the ST I was with that day that I had a production studio in my house and wrote and sang my own songs. I told her I wrote both the melody and lyrics, and laid down the guitar track on the recordings. She wanted to hear one and I happened to have a playlist of some of my work on my iPhone, so I played one for her. She must have reported this to the boss lady I was with today, because she also asked me to play one of my songs. So, I did. After the song was over, I got my final surprise. She asked me to sing the same song for her. I was totally intimidated since I had gained some confidence concerning conversing with people, but I just assumed that my singing days were over due to the stroke. But this lady convinced me that I could do it, so I finally agreed. I sang it for her, expecting to stumble through it. I was totally surprised when I sang it, and the song sounded virtually the same to me. I mentioned this and she smiled and told me that I had made quite a bit if progress in the time I was here. We then played the song I had sung a second time, and sure enough, the studio version did sound almost identical to the one I had just sung. Wow! Now, if I can regain my skill on the guitar, I'll be set. The session ended shortly after that, but I guess my evaluation was made while I was singing my song. In retrospect, I think it was genius. I had to correctly do all the lip, mouth, tongue, timing, spacing, enunciation, and breathing necessary to sing the song and have the sound be so close to my studio version. There may not, at least in my case, have been a better way to evaluate me than the way it was done. The added benefit for me was that now I knew I would still be able to sing. Another victory for me. A little while later, I was talking to a floor nurse and she told me I would be leaving in the morning, so I guess I did pass all the evaluations. I am more than ready to go home.

Day Thirty-One. Well, I have just completed Part 2 of my Stroke journey. Part 1 was checking into the hospital to be stabilized and maybe have my life saved. Part 2 was checking in to this facility to rehab me back to being functional again. Both the hospital and the rehab center have done their job, so next week I start Part 3, Outpatient Therapy, with a new

Occupational Therapist and a new Physical Therapist. My OT at this facility got my right upper body to the point where it is almost completely functional again, and I walked unaided yesterday, due to my PT's magic, but now I need to get fine-tuned. That's what I imagine Outpatient Therapy will be doing during my future visits. I can't wait. My doctor has told me that the staff at the Outpatient Clinic are just as professional, talented, and motivated as the staff here. Over the next few months, I am going to dedicate myself to following their advice to the letter. As I assess my body now, I know that I still need to work on increasing the rotation of my right wrist, strengthening the grip of my right hand, increasing the flexibility of the fingers on that hand, and strengthening my right leg so I can start to take multiple steps laterally. I am ready to do whatever it takes. I also know that I have to fix several glitches in my gait, before I can even think about completely giving up my walker. But again, I am ready to do whatever it takes. I have several new short-term goals now. I want to have tripled my grip strength, be walking totally unaided, and be able to toss a tennis ball correctly and hit a serve by the end of my sessions at the Outpatient Therapy Clinic. That's about two months. If willpower is the deciding factor, I will hit those goals. I say goodbye to the weekend staff, and then I am wheeled to the main entrance where Patty is waiting for me in her car. I guess my PT was right, because I walk the few feet from the entrance to the passenger side of the car unaided. There is a handle right over the passenger seat, so I grab it with my left hand and maneuver myself into the seat with no difficulty. Once again, I am glad I am left-handed because it made entering the car much easier. We now head home to do our best to make our home "fall-proof," especially the bathroom. But we have followed all of my OT's recommendations, so hopefully we are ready. More than anything, I will be happy to sleep in my own bed. I'll need lots of quality sleep to maintain my strength as I begin Part 3. My first date at the new Outpatient Therapy facility is next Tuesday, and I am scheduled two days a week. Each day I go, I will spend one hour with a new Occupational Therapist, and then immediately spend a second hour with a new Physical Therapist. So, I basically will be going through the same routine as I did when I checked into this Inpatient facility.

3. FINE TUNING DURING OUTPATIENT REHAB

Day Thirty-Five. I immediately run into my first roadblock. I need a ride to the facility each day I am scheduled. Patty is my chauffer today, but she will be working during my future session dates. Friends have offered to drive me, and I thought I was going to have to take them up on their kind offer, but it bothers me a little to know I will be disrupting their schedule to give me a ride. Luckily, as soon as I tell my new OT about my problem, she informs me that the facility has a car pickup and drop off service for people in my position. She immediately arranges for this service to provide me with round trip transportation for the dates of my visits. These guys are good.

So, today is my first encounter with the facility, which is conveniently located 15 minutes from my house. When I arrive, using my walker, I am met at the main entrance by my new OT. She will be doing most of my weekly sessions with me. She escorts me back to her therapy area and, after she straightens out my transportation issue, does a thorough evaluation of my present condition, just like my last OT did. This includes evaluating my right shoulder, elbow, wrist, hand, and finger grip. She also has me do two timed finger dexterity tests. One in which I have to remove pegs from a small pegboard using my right hand only, and another where I have to place different pegs into a larger pegboard. In both exercises she tests both my left-hand time and my right-hand time for an initial comparison. As expected, it takes me much longer when doing these tests with my right hand versus my left. She measures my grip strength and it is 35 pounds of force. Over 50% higher than when my OT at the Inpatient facility first measured it, but still much lower than my left, which is 110 pounds of force. My new OT also notes the reduced wrist rotation of my right wrist, my inability to totally straighten my right arm, and the somewhat limited Range of Motion (ROM) of my right shoulder. No surprises there, the OT at the Inpatient facility had done a great job of getting me to this point, considering I was virtually paralyzed when she started. My new OT also notes that I am able to rotate my right wrist to the "tennis ball" position, but only hold it there for 10 - 15 seconds before it starts to turn back to the left, despite my best effort to stop it. So, she has several areas to help me improve on. She told me that on the next visit she planned on using an electronic device that used electrodes, in this case attached to my right forearm, to stimulate the nerves that control the movement of my right wrist and hand (E-stim), to help with my neuromuscular Re-education. We would also concentrate on strengthening and coordination exercises for that area and also my shoulder. I have read about E-stim, and how effective it can be, so I am extremely curious to see what effect it will have on my right hand, leg and foot. Our hour was up, so I retrieved my walker and headed over to meet my new Physical

Therapist. She also did a thorough evaluation of me. Since I was warmed up, she had me do 5 Sit to Stands, which is just like it sounds. I sit on a chair, and then stand, then sit and stand again – as fast as I can. It took me a little over 8 seconds to do a set of 5. She did several tests of my stride and balance, including having me walk on a level surface (the floor) as well as climb stairs while holding a railing, which I did fine, and without holding a railing, which I was unable to do. She also had me stand on one leg, both my left (3 seconds) and my right (I could barely do 1 second), and stand with my feet together and then first with my right in front, and then my left in front, all with my eyes first open and then closed. She also tested several of my lower body muscle groups for strength and flexibility. We talked a little about how future sessions would work, and she told me that as far as the next session we would work on strengthening my right leg, and do some work on Neuromuscular re-education, as well as my balance and cardiovascular endurance. She also told me that I would be given a Home Exercise Program during my next visit which I needed to faithfully follow, which was music to my ears. I had hoped for some ideas on what to do at home and now that hope would become a reality. Everything my new PT said sounded good to me since I definitely, after she finished her evaluation, saw many areas I was going to have to improve in, with everything she had listed topping my "must improve" list. The session was over so I retrieved my trusty walker and headed out.

Day Thirty-Seven. I am still dependent on my walker when I want to move around. I'm still a way from walking any distance without it. Today I spent my 1st ten minutes warming up on a machine similar to the Elliptical I used before. This one is smaller and for arms only, and I pedal it with my hands. Forward for 5 minutes and in reverse for 5 minutes. Then she has me use a piece of equipment called a Saeboglide. This is a short exercise bar which works out my right arm by having me grasp a sleeve which glides over the bar, allowing me to perform various controlled right arm exercises. Right away I am impressed with this device. It is extremely versatile. I am going to add it to my "must have" list for my home program. My OT then does E-stim on my right forearm for 10 minutes to stimulate the nerves that are responsible for the rotation of my right hand that I have had so much trouble with. I am fascinated by the E-stim. The system's electrodes are strategically placed next to the muscle group or groups that contribute to different actions like hand rotation or foot flexion. The process stimulates the sometimes-dormant nerves, which in turn cause the corresponding muscles to start moving. Muscles that hadn't been moving before. The E-stim doesn't have an immediate effect on my right-hand rotation, but I am very excited to see what effect it has on my right foot, which still won't flex very much, and my toes, which barely move as well. Then my OT gives me a weighted bar to hold in my right hand and then rotate the hand to the maximum I am able, in both directions. We then work with an Upper Body Rotation device, just like the one I used at the inpatient center. We place the rubber tip on the floor to do horizontal shoulder rotations, and then on the wall to do vertical rotations. My OT is definitely covering all the areas of my right side that need some work. When I rotate over to my PT, she spends quite a bit of time on my right hip and right knee flexion. We work on helping me make sure my muscles fire in the right order when walking for 8-10 minutes. She has me use parallel bars for support so I can take longer steps, still concentrating on correct hip and knee flexion. After that we returned to working the muscles om the back of my right thigh. There is already no question in my mind that her focus on my right hip and knee is having a positive effect on my gait. For one thing the muscles in my right leg are getting tired, while at the same time, my gait is improving, which means to me that we are working muscles that needed to be pushed a little. She next introduces me to a green OPTP Stretch Out Strap and teaches me to use it to stretch my hip, upper thigh, and calf, as well as assist me during my attempt to flex my toes upward, by helping stretch the tissue in the sole of my foot (plantar facia). We finished the session by doing E-stim on muscles on the outside of my lower leg that are involved in proper toe flexing. When using the E-stim machine she would increase the current to the electrodes attached to me to the point where I could really feel it, then stop increasing it and leave the high setting at the point I told her to stop. At that point the machine would cycle on and off somewhere around every 10 seconds. Once the machine started cycling on and off, when I felt the maximum current in my leg, I would simultaneously flex my right foot and toes upward, as hard as I could, and then relax when the current dropped. She allowed the machine to run for 10 minutes, after which she disconnected the electrodes. During the E-stim I immediately noticed that I was able to flex my right foot and toes 1 – 2 inches higher than I had ever been able to before. Once it was over, my toes still maintained their increased flexibility. So, in my first E-stim session I had a positive result. With my foot and toes now flexing further upward when I walked, the toe drag that still bothered me from time-to-time ceased to occur. This is a big victory for me and one step closer to getting my right step closer to my left. I am impressed with E-stim.

Day Forty-One. I have now got my schedule worked out with the car service. They drop me at the main entrance and I use my walker to make my way to the general workout area. My OT starts me with some stretching and then 10 minutes on their Elliptical to warm up my upper body. We then work hard on my shoulder, which is very tight and causing me some discomfort. We do a variety of shoulder rotation and flexion using green and yellow bands and a 3-pound bar. Next is a group of exercises on the Saeboglide. When those are finished, we work my wrists by having me grasp one of the parallel bars and doing a variety of stretches. In certain positions, the stretches cause discomfort in my right shoulder. We then focus on my wrist. First, she has me roll a ball of putty using a small weighted bar held only in my right hand, until it is flat. Then we practice right and left rotation of my right wrist using a 2-pound weight, and my forearm resting on the arm of the chair I am sitting in. I then switch to my PT, who first puts me on a different Elliptical for 10 minutes to warm up my legs. I then do a series of thigh muscle stretches with my PT's assistance, and also a series of stretches focusing on the back of my leg, from knee to ankle. We then do some right-side bridging exercises in which I lay flat on my back, and raise my hips. My PT helps me by holding my right foot in place on the table I am on. I then practice walking as she watches to evaluate my steps and after a few minutes we switch to the parallel bars where I take larger steps to help me correctly do the hip and knee flexion portion of my step. I then, once more do a variety of stretches targeting the back of my right leg, and then we finish up the last 10 minutes with the E-stim on my lower leg, to again try to increase the amount of upward flexing I can do with my right foot. I definitely feel that I am making progress during both sessions, with the improvement in my right foot and toe movement, and, as a result, my overall gait, topping the list.

Day Forty-Three. I start with 10 minutes on their upper body Elliptical to warm up. Then I do an exercise where I hold a short section of one of their green rubber exercise bands in both hands at mid-body level and then pull back my hands and try to squeeze together my shoulder blades. Next, I do the same thing except I try to extend my shoulders forward and upward while still holding the green band in the same position. Then it's on to my now-faithful Saeboglide. When I started with my PT, I warmed up my legs on a 2nd Elliptical and then with her identifying which muscle group should be firing at that particular moment, she coached me on the proper hip and knee flexion that had to occur for me to have the proper gait. We then went to the parallel bars and worked on proper hip and knee flexion some more, with me taking exaggerated steps. We then went to the exercise bed and I did sets of leg curls. I am curling my foot higher each time, so the stretches we do for the back of my right leg are paying off. The E-stim is also paying off. We did a session again today, and I am able to my right foot further upward each time we use it. As a result, there is a noticeable improvement in my gait.

Day Forty-Eight. Today my OT and I worked more on shoulder blade retraction. We also worked more on me rotating my right hand to the maximum I was able and then holding that position as long as possible. We had me hold a small weighted bar to assist me in maintaining the fully rotated position. Today while with my PT, we rigged up a solution to a problem I was having with my gait where my right toes were pointing in and to the left versus slightly out and to the right. We took a short piece of the black rubber exercise band and tied it in a loop to the end of an OTPT Stretch Out Strap we used routinely. I then slipped my right foot into the loop and placed the other end of the green band over my left shoulder. I then pulled down on the green band with my left hand, being sure to not create so much tension that my right knee would hyperextend. Pulling the Strap down over my left shoulder caused the loop at the other end to pull the front of my right foot out and to the right, ensuring it was oriented correctly, versus pointing in. I put just enough tension on the band so that I could still walk, although my right toes were now pointed out. It worked really well at teaching my right foot the correct angle to have as I walked unaided. It worked so well that I bought the materials and made a duplicate to practice with at home. Today we did our now normal E-stim session, which continues to help me increase the flexibility of my right foot. However, with my permission, my PT also did what is called dry needling on the largest muscle in my upper thigh, and part of the big muscle in the back of the lower leg, to decrease muscle tightness. It doesn't hurt, and is somewhat similar to acupuncture. When she locates a tight spot in the muscle with a needle, the muscle twitches, signifying that the tension has been released. She located several tense areas in my thigh muscle. I noticed when she found a tense area immediately because my leg would twitch involuntarily. I was able to walk quite a bit freer after she reduced the tension in my thigh muscle. I am really impressed with the work we are doing. The modified OTPT Stretch Out

Strap, and needling, are two more things we did to my leg that had immediate results. Two things in one day. I am really getting much closer to walking on my own thanks to my PT's talent.

Day Fifty. I do my 10 minutes of warmups on the upper body Elliptical, and then start using the Upper Body Rotation device to do shoulder rotations. After that we use a variety of their colored exercise bands to continue my shoulder workout. Once I have completed the shoulder exercises, I go through my Saeboglide routine, then I do some work on my grip, including squeezing exercises on one of their larger hand gripper devices. Then my OT has me do a new task. She gives me a ball of putty which has 10 pennies buried within it. She instructs me, using only my right hand, to find and remove all the pennies from the putty. I do this exercise a few times, and it is harder than it looks to flatten the putty in sections to search for the coins and then remove them. Finally, after several sets, my wrist begins to fatigue, and we have to stop. Today my OT also presents me with a great set of finger strength and dexterity challenges. I still have work to do. Today with my PT, after warming up on the 2nd Elliptical, we once again did both E-stim on my right lower leg, and then dry needling to my thigh to decrease tightness. There are once again multiple twitches in the muscle as she does the needling.

Day Fifty-Five. Today I only have a session with my PT. After warming up on the Elliptical, she has me do several minutes of a complete new set of hip stretches while kneeling on a foam pad. These stretches are so effective that I am now going to include all of them in my home workout program. We then practice walking, again paying special attention to my hip and knee flexion. We then return to the parallel bars and have me exaggerate my steps so as to get the firing of the hip and knee happening at exactly the right time. Finally, while I am laying on my back on an exercise bed, my PT manually moves my right leg to improve my hip flex coordination and speed. While I am still on the bed, I also do curls to strengthen the muscles in the back of my upper leg. She then does another E-stim session on my lower leg.

Day Fifty-Seven. I just meet with my PT again today. After warming up on the 2nd Elliptical, we spend a few minutes with her assisting me in using the OTPT Stretch Out Strap to really stretch out my thigh and calf muscles. Then we started balance work. First, I did 3 sets of heel and toe raises to try to get my right foot to flex as much as my left. Then we worked on perfecting my hip/knee flexing with my PT again helping me. I then returned to the parallel bars and practiced the large step routine, this time adding the appropriate arm swing to the steps for better balance. I then went through my standard rear-leg stretches in preparation for practicing my gait. At the end of the session, I was really getting fatigued, which tells me I need to work harder at home on my overall endurance.

Day Sixty-Two. After my 10-minute warmup today, my OT had me work on squeezing my shoulder blades together while holding a short green rubber exercise band to provide resistance. Then we spend a lot of time working on my right elbow with a 3-pound weight in front of a mirror, to help me make sure I am standing correctly and that my posture is correct. Then we practice some coordination drills in which we threw balls to each other, starting with a plastic hollow golf ball and then graduating to a soccer ball. We then did an exercise where she tossed the ball to me and I was to hit it with a lightweight bar I was holding in my right hand. I was able to hit the ball all 20 times it was thrown at me. And, finally, we tested the rotation of my right hand and wrist, and found that we had now worked them to the point where I could hold a tennis ball in my palm and toss it into the air as though going through a real serving motion. So, I had one less goal to achieve. I then talked to my OT about how I had brought my tennis racquet and a bag of balls to multiple sessions at the Inpatient facility and asked her if I could do the same at this facility. She agreed, so I will be bringing everything to our next session.

Day Sixty-Four. Today we started doing my "play tennis" protocol. We did it outside, with a PT throwing me balls to the left and right, just out of my reach and making me step to the ball to hit a return. It was good to get back to stepping both left and right and hitting forehands and backhands. I can definitely notice an improvement in my ability to take one, or even 2 steps in any direction, including forwards or backwards, without losing my balance. I have especially improved in stepping with my right foot. I can flex the foot so much better now, since the E-stim and dry needling. Those procedures have really helped speed up my recovery. I had a short session with my OT today due to a transportation problem, so after the tennis exercise and my Saeboglide routine, I moved to my PT. She informed me that she was going to do a re-evaluation of me today, noting changes from when I started a month ago. We started with five Sit to Stands, which I did in a tiny bit over 5 seconds, a big improvement from 8+ seconds a month ago. When my PT monitored my ability to walk long distances (40') I received a score of 4 out of 5, compared to 3 out of 5 a month ago. When she had me stand on just my right leg, I increased from less than a second a month ago to 4 seconds today. My PT also noted a significant increase in the flexibility in my hip and upper leg muscles. Their flexibility now almost matches my left leg. My right leg still shows a significant lack of coordination, although that may have been partially due to me being fatigued from the tennis exercise. To summarize my overall progress, the following short-term goals were set and have since been met by my PT and I since she first started working with me one month ago. They include: 1) I will be able to walk 500' with less than 5/10 total fatigue – MET. 2) I will be able to walk 800' without the walker with less than 3/10 total fatigue – MET. 3) I will increase the strength of my right leg by 50% - MET. 4) I will perform a Home Exercise Program to increase right leg strength and endurance – MET. There are still several long-term goals involving my overall balance and right leg strength that have only been partially met, which we will be working to complete in the coming month.

Day Sixty-Nine. Today my OT is evaluating me. I'm still showing weakness in my upper right side. And some lack of rotation of my right wrist and hand. My right grip strength is still at 35. After the evaluation I did 10 minutes on the Elliptical, followed by my Saeboglide routine, and then I got on a mat and my OT had me practice reaching with my left hand, while on my hands and knees, as I held myself up with my right. She told me that this exercise was part of my Neuromuscular re-education. We then did some shoulder rotation exercises using Red FlintRehab Resistance Bars. We then did grip strengthening using an adjustable tension hand gripper which I really liked. I am definitely going to order one of these hand grippers for my home workouts. We then wrapped up the session with some finger dexterity exercises using small pegs. I then went to my session with my PT. Today was a repeat of our last session, with her and I working on perfecting my hip/knee flexing. I then returned to the parallel bars and practiced the long step routine, again adding the appropriate arm swing to my steps for better balance. I then went through my standard leg stretches. While I was on the exercise table, I rolled to my back and my PT assisted me in doing hip flexing at various speeds to help improve my coordination and speed of leg movement. We then did an E-stim session, again concentrating on my right lower leg, to continue to improve my right foot upward flexing.

Day Seventy-One. Today I created a major breakthrough. I parked my walker for good. From now on I will be walking. I feel strong enough to make it from the front entrance to the therapy workout area. So today I entered the facility on foot and walked to the workout area. My OT was at her desk, so not in my line of sight when I entered. When I walked up to her, she undoubtedly thought I had parked my walker as usual, since in the past, whenever I was working within the facility I always walked. I didn't make a big deal about it, and started telling her about the pain I was experiencing in my right shoulder, perhaps from overwork since I was also working at home. She acknowledged my pain and she took it into consideration during our session. We first did some of what my OT termed Neuromuscular re-education. She had me lean on a large ball with my right arm extended as far as I could, very close in appearance to a chest CPR position. This actually was very good for my elbow and wrist and I could feel, especially in my wrist, that I was getting a good stretch. We also worked on my grip strength with the large, spring-loaded hand exerciser, as well as working individual fingers using a smaller one designed so any finger could be exercised separately.

She had me work my wrists by doing what's called a prayer stretch where I rest my elbows on a table with my hands together like I'm praying. I then lower my hands straight down toward the table while sliding my elbows away from me in a line parallel to my body. As my hands drop and get closer to the table, I get a good flex/stretch in my wrists. I especially felt it in my weak right wrist. I really like this stretch, and will be adding it to my home routine. We then did finger dexterity and strengthening in my right hand and fingers by manipulating red putty, maneuvering it with my right hand only as I pulled dimes from it. I still have significant finger weakness, and have only menial control over my ring finger. My little finger I have almost no control over. Our session was over so I went to work with my PT. She had remarked on Tuesday that she knew of a special foot taping technique which would inhibit my right lower leg muscles and improve movement in my right ankle and toes. I was all for it because my lack of toe movement was the only thing in my lower right leg area that wasn't working right. So, my PT taped my right foot and immediately I could feel changes in my toes. To increase the effect of the taping, she did another E-stim session on my lower right leg, this time for 15 minutes. At the end of the E-stim session, once the tape was removed, I really seemed to have more control over my right toes. When I tried to flex my right foot, I was able to bend my toes upward more than I was ever able to in the past. It appears that another of my PT's techniques is going to improve my walking. This is a big deal, because the only trouble I have during my walks at home is my toes clearing small elevations like a 1" change in height in the sidewalk. I am still at the point because of my toes not moving, that I walk my route through the neighborhood with my eyes on the ground in front of me, instead of looking straight ahead, so I can see those 1" variations and exaggerate the elevation of my right foot so I won't trip over them. This newfound "toe freedom" is exactly what I was looking for.

Day Seventy-Six. Today with my OT, we worked all of my right side. We worked on my fingers once again with the smaller finger exerciser. My OT used E-stim for 10 minutes to release my tight right wrist, and decrease the pain I had been experiencing in that arm. This wrist flexor release also provides me with better wrist extension and rotation. I then did several Saeboglide exercises for my right arm and wrist, and then went right to a variety of blue exercise bands to work with resistance on shoulder extension, rotation, and retraction of my shoulder blades. We also did some wrist strengthening exercises by twisting the Green FlintRehab Resistance Bar. Today with my PT we started with some modified and regular lunges to loosen up my thigh muscles, especially my right thigh. My right knee flexion seemed much easier once we stretched my thigh. I am definitely walking better every week. Next, we went through another session where she taped my right foot to inhibit my right lower leg muscles, so as to provide more right toe flexibility and increased upward flexing of the right foot. And we did another E-stim session to enhance the impact of the taping. When I get home, I am going to add the modified upper leg lunge to my workout. It really helps my right leg to relax, which is a vital part of getting my gait perfected. I must stay relaxed.

Day Seventy-Eight. I have been aware, for some time now, that the stroke has had an effect on my emotions. In particular, I get slightly "anxious" much more than in my pre-stroke life. But I have recently found out that the slightest emotional stress makes me slightly tense and disrupts my gait. For my gait to be at its best, I must be relaxed. I am really working hard to return my general emotional state to what it used to be. It is definitely a challenge. So, to help my body be totally relaxed, which I have found it needs to be in order to make my right leg function properly, yesterday I went for my first professional massage since I had my stroke. It definitely relaxed me, and is something I intend to have done twice a week from now on. In another week, I will be on my own, and regular massages will become a part of my new routine. Today with my OT, after my 10-minute warmup, we worked quite a bit on my finger grip and overall hand strength. Such as pulling small balls through green putty, and rolling the putty into a ball, all with only my right hand. We also did some additional wrist strengthening by having me support my weight solely with my right arm on one of the exercise tables. With my PT today, after warming up, we did a series of stretches and exercises for hip, thigh and back of leg strength stability, and coordination. Once we were finished and I walked around the room, I noticed less tension in my right knee. It was more relaxed. Maybe because of the massage? Today, my PT also began having me do a series of lateral step exercises. It is quite a bit easier now, due to her help, with all the new procedures she has provided, then it was when I first convinced the Inpatient Center to let me practice my tennis game there. I can step laterally, forward at an angle, or backwards now without fear. Although still with a great amount of caution. Since I stored my walker for good, I have been walking more each day and going through my exercise program at home, which has some portions where I move forward at an angle and laterally, so now it's something I am used to after the lateral exercises. My PT taped my foot again and did one more session of E-stim to enhance the effect. The upward flexing of my right foot gets better each time we do this, and walking also becomes easier.

Day Eighty-Three. Today with my OT we used the Upper Body Rotation device, resting on the floor, for rotating and flexing my shoulder. For other shoulder exercises and practicing weight shift, we used a medium sized therapy ball while seated, and a 3-pound weighted bar. My OT did one more 10-minute E-stim session on my right forearm again to release the tight wrist muscles to allow for increased right wrist rotation and extension. Then it was on to my Saeboglide routine, which is really working. When I start my session with my PT, we work on my gait. She has me work with the modified OTPT Stretch Out Strap again to encourage my right foot to turn out to the right, and to ensure proper knee flexion. We also have another E-stim session on my lower leg to help give me even more foot flexing ability.

Day Eighty-Five. Today is my last session of Outpatient Therapy. After today I will be on my own. During my session with my OT, we work all phases of shoulder rehab, including shoulder blade retraction with the blue exercise band supplying the resistance. We do finger strengthening by me using my right hand only to find and remove coins from a mass of green putty, and a finger "walking exercise where I am tasked with scrunching up a small hand towel. These exercises used to challenge me, but they seem much easier now. For my fine motor skills, I practice manipulating a tennis ball with my right fingertips, and also untie knots from a single shoelace using just my right hand. I tried this exercise a few weeks ago and got nowhere, but today I am able to untie all the knots with my right hand only. For grip strengthening I use the Green FlintRehab Resistance Bar. We don't take a measurement of my grip, but I do later that day at home, and it has risen to the mid-40s. it was at 35 when I started here. During my last session with my PT, she concentrates on working on my right ankle and right toes to increase their flexing and to improve my right foot's ability to point out to the right versus in to the left. She tapes my foot one last time to enhance the effect of what she is trying to accomplish. I also did the side-stepping exercises I had been practicing.

I anticipated getting the right side of my body fine-tuned at this facility, and I wasn't disappointed. My progress, especially as a result of my PT's ingenuity, has been amazing. Several of the solutions she arrived at to help me, were of her own creation. By solving my problem where my right toes pointed in, to the left, versus out, to the right, she literally shaved months off my recovery time. Also, the hip and upper leg stretches that she modified specifically for me, shaved off several more weeks. There is no way I will be able to properly thank her, other than expressing my un-dying gratitude. In addition to these "custom" solutions, the E-stim and taping of my right foot have me almost back to my pre-stroke walking gait. Now it's time to push myself hard at home, so I can keep my promise to myself, and play two sets of tennis on the one-year anniversary of my stroke. I'm sure, based on my progress so far, that the home workouts I have created will give me the chance to keep my promise. My workout area at home has now become my new battlefield. Time for me to push the envelope. My new goal is to be able to run 4-5 steps in any direction, by Day 335. Today I can't run at all, but, then, it wasn't that long ago that I couldn't walk at all.

I have been having the car service drop me off

at the parking entrance to the facility for the last few weeks, so I can warm up a little by walking the last 40 yards to the front entrance. When I was walking those 40 yards today, a lady, coming from another area of the parking lot, joined me and asked, "are you here to pick up someone?" She had no idea that I had suffered a stroke. To her, I was just walking in, like anybody else. I told her a little lie, and said, "Yes, as a matter of fact, I am." Then we entered the facility together. That wonderful lady had just made my year, without knowing it.

Anything's possible. Tennis, here I come.

4. GETTING BACK ON THE ROAD

Day Ninety-Two. Today Patty and I visited my doctor so that I could have a complete physical. He and I felt the physical was necessary before I resumed driving. The physical included a series of mental tests as well as testing of my reaction time, the flex ability of my right foot to ensure it was more than enough to quickly go from gas to brake, and all aspects of my vision including peripheral vision. I passed all of the tests easily, and he cleared me to drive. He also wrote out his approval on a prescription slip and gave it to me to keep in my wallet. Just in case. This was one more goal achieved. Now, I need to continue my workouts at home so I can meet my goal to play tennis again. Part of my workout is working on the rotation of my right hand even though I can turn it enough now to toss a tennis ball in the air. I want to train my right hand to rotate even further so I don't have to think about the toss at all. I want to put that portion of my game on autopilot, like it used to be.

5. SETTLING IN TO MY NEW LIFESTYLE

Day One Hundred Twenty-Two. I have now been doing my home "Stroke Workouts" (I created two which work different area of my body, that I do on alternate days), for one month. Three days a week during the month I have also been doing what I call my Forward/Lateral movement & Quick-step session, a 30-minute session to practice moving left, right, forward or backward at different angles, from a fixed starting position, as though returning a serve in tennis. This session also includes 10 minutes of "running" (really more like shuffling) back and forth down a 45' marble hallway in my home. The Stroke Workout includes individual exercises for all the troublesome parts of my right side as well as general exercises for both sides. The Forward/Lateral movement & Quick-step session is strictly for my legs. Before starting either one, I go through a 15-minute period of warm-up and stretching, using my OPTP Stretch Out Strap, which really helps with my gait and the Starktape Foot and Leg Stretcher which due to its design, really helps me increase the flexing of my right foot. My Stroke Workout includes using the FlintRehab Resistance Bar Hand and Fore Arm Exerciser to increase my grip strength. I like the FlintRehab Resistance Bars because I can twist or bend them either horizontally or vertically to help strengthen my right wrist. I started with their Red bar which has a lower resistance, and when my grip became sufficient to twist the bar without my hand slipping, I graduated to the

Green bar which has more resistance. At the rate I am going, I will soon be ready to move up to the Blue. When I started my Stroke Workouts a month ago my grip strength was approximately 45 pounds. In 30 days of faithfully using the Green FlintRehab Resistance Bar and a generic spring-loaded hand exerciser, it has increased to a solid 55 pounds. I measure my grip strength several times a week. For the majority of my workout, I use Starktape flat rubber exercise bands, cut to specific lengths, a second set of Starktape exercise bands made of tubing which contain handles, end clips, and a door-anchor, and a set of soft hand weights, which vary from 3 – 5 pounds in weight. I like the soft weights because they are easier to grip with my still weak right hand. For my arm and shoulder, I mainly do rotational exercises where, without holding any weight, I rotate my arm (and by default my shoulder) in full circles in front of my body, clockwise and then counterclockwise, and then do the same rotations on the right side of my body. I also do a tennis ball toss with my right hand to work even more on control and flexibility. I simply simulate the position I would be in if I were to serve in a real game, and toss the tennis ball gently upward to strengthen my arm and shoulder, and develop the "touch" to toss the ball to the appropriate height. The toss is getting easier by the week, but I still remember, two months ago, when I wasn't able to toss, or even hold the ball in my right hand. If I hadn't spent all those hours rehabbing my hand, I wouldn't have been able to do this exercise, which is a good one in general for getting my weak shoulder, arm, wrist, hand, and fingers to work together. As the last part of that exercise, I try to catch the ball in my right hand when it drops, to work on my dexterity and hand-eye coordination. Nothing complicated, and nothing dangerous. As far as my Forward/Lateral movement & Quick Step routine, I only do those sessions with a spotter. Whether I am taking multiple steps to either side, or shuffling down my hallway at the same speed as my spotter's fast walk, I always have somebody ready to catch me if I start to fall. I haven't fallen yet, but I'm not leaving anything to chance. I have, however, made great progress with my Forward/Lateral movement & Quick Step routine. When I started, from a simulated position of waiting to receive a tennis serve, I could move one quick, large step to my left, right, one quick, large step forward, and one slow normal-sized step backward. In the last 30 days, I have increased to two steps left, right, and forward, and two more cautious steps to the rear. And, I believe I will soon be able to increase that to three. When I first started my hallway "runs," it took me 14 strides to go from one end to the other. In the last 30 days, I have dropped the number of strides to twelve. My stride is getting longer. If this rate of decrease continues, in a few more months I should be able to do my run/shuffle from the middle of a court to either side. So, perhaps my goal of playing at least a semblance of tennis on the one-year anniversary of my stroke will be achieved

6. SIX MONTHS AFTER MY STROKE

Day One Hundred Eighty-Five. I have now been doing my home "Stroke Workouts" for three months. I have also been doing my Forward/Lateral movement & Quick-step sessions for three months. Before starting either one, I still go through my 15-minute period of warm-up and stretching, using my OPTP Stretch Out Strap and Starktape Foot and Leg stretcher, and still use the FlintRehab Resistance Bar Hand and Fore Arm Exerciser. I have graduated to the Blue FlintRehab Resistance Bar. Two months ago, my grip strength was averaging around 55 pounds. It is now averaging 65 pounds. For the majority of my workout, I still use the Starktape flat rubber exercise bands and tubing with handles and a door-anchor, and my soft hand weights, which I have now increased in some cases to 10 pounds. As far as my Forward/Lateral Movement & Quick Step routine, two months ago, I could move two steps left, right, and forward, and two more cautious steps to the rear. I have now increased the number of steps in all directions to four. Two months ago, my hallway "runs," for which I still use a spotter, took me twelve strides to go from one end to the other. I have now dropped the number of strides to ten. My stride continues to get longer. I've also experienced two breakthroughs in the last sixty days. The first is that my guitar-playing skills are coming back. So far, I can only strum, I can't pick, and I'm not nearly as fast and smooth as I was, but I can get through the rhythm of any song I know. I give most of the credit to scrunching up the scarf literally hundreds of times. That simple exercise paid huge dividends. The second breakthrough is that I have been to the tennis club. Granted, I worked up the courage to go there just to see if I could serve the ball, not to run. But I went. It turned out that not only can I toss the ball correctly, but after a little experimentation with my footwork, I was actually able to hit a serve into the opponent's serve box. I was even putting a little spin on the ball towards the end. The other important thing to note is that I didn't have any balance issues. I was able to go through my normal service motion without feeling like I was going to fall. The only adjustment I really had to make was to keep both feet flat on the court during the ball toss versus my old stance where I had my front foot toes pointed up and the foot balanced on its heel. It was not that long ago that I couldn't take a step in any direction without losing my balance, and I couldn't even hold the ball in my right hand. I ended up hitting about 50 balls, and then I ran out of gas. But I served. Now I have to go back 2-3 more times to make sure I can do it every time. If that is the case, I will get someone to hit me balls and see if I can do my 4-step Forward/Lateral movement & Quick Step routine on the court, instead of just at home. The interesting thing here is that I ran out of gas from wandering around the court picking up balls I had hit. That simple task still tired me out. I still have to do a lot of work on my endurance. But from where I was on Day One, being outside in the fresh air, doing something I truly love to do, is a wonderful thing.

7. NINE MONTHS AFTER MY STROKE

Day Two Hundred Seven-Two. I have now been doing my home "Stroke Workouts," and my Forward/Lateral movement & Quick-step sessions for six months. I still go through my 15-minute warm-up and stretching period using my OPTP Stretch Out Strap, Starktape Foot and Leg stretcher, and Blue FlintRehab Resistance Bar - Hand and Fore Arm Exerciser. And, I continue to make progress in virtually all areas. For example, my grip strength has increased to between 70 and 75 pounds. Plus, I am now doing leg curls on a leg machine, and am up to 25-pound curls for my thighs, and 10-pound curls for the back of my legs, which I can now raise to a full vertical position. I have increased my number of steps in all directions from four, three months ago, to six, and I have decreased the number of strides in my "hallway run," from 10 to 9. So, my stride is still getting longer. And, my cardio has increased substantially. I can get through any workout without feeling exhausted.

And, I continue to go to the tennis club once or twice a week to practice my serve, which is continuing to improve but I am not ready to start practicing yet, because one more temporary roadblock has been placed in front of me. My right leg is not ready to "run." Earlier today, 9 months since my stroke, I got together with one of the coaches at the club, to set up a date to start the long road back. He had a few minutes free, so

1ˢᵗ he watched my serve and approved of what he saw. Then he took a basket of balls, and dropped them 1-2 strides away from me and watched my forehand and backhand, which, considering the time I had been gone, were pretty good. Then he stood at the net and tossed the balls 4-5 strides away from me, at close to game speed, and watched me as I tried to run after them. The key word here is TRIED. What he saw, and I experienced, right away, was that my right toes, foot, and ankle, were not yet strong enough to support my complete body weight. After the 3ʳᵈ step, my right ankle buckled. It didn't matter which way I ran, the buckling occurred in any direction I went. Right then we knew I wasn't ready. All my hallway running and toe raise exercises were more than enough to get me walking, but were not nearly enough to prepare me for, full sprint, direction-changing, stop-and-start, tennis running. I thanked him for his time and went home to go back to war. I'm really not that upset, since it is only 9 months since my stroke. I'm still happy with where I am. Actually, I am happy that I discovered this running problem now, since I can develop a new workout plan to address it. And, that's what I just finished doing. I've modified my Quick Step program to include several exercises to strengthen that whole area. The key is, that while standing with just my fingertips against a wall, I have to get to the point where I can hook my left foot over the heel of my right, and do sets of 10 toe lifts, where I can raise my entire body, just using my right toes. I've already tried it, and I can only do one right now. Plus, my knee also starts to shake after I do one, so some of the new exercises are for my knee. I now have a new goal to hit before I even get to my primary goal of playing tennis. I am going to seriously strengthen my right side, from toes to knee. I have not let my weakened right side stop me yet. I'm certainly not going to let it happen when I am this close. I'm going back to war.

8. TEN MONTHS AFTER MY STROKE

Day Three Hundred Five. I have now been doing my modified Quick-step workout for a month. I have made a fair amount of progress with strengthening my right toes, ankle, and knee, but I am far from the day when I will be able to do sets of ten. Right now, one set of 5 is all I can manage, and the set of 5 is while I'm wearing a knee brace to prevent the possibility of hyperextending my knee. I spoke with my Primary Care Physician, and he strongly recommended that I wear it. The increase in strength in that whole area is substantial, compared to just 30 days ago. I have not tried running at the tennis club since I started, but am heading over in two days to see how I do compared to last time. I feel much stronger, so I think I will be much improved. Only two days to wait.

9. ELEVEN MONTHS AFTER MY STROKE

Day Three Hundred Thirty-Three. Sorry, I am a little late with this entry. Just about a month ago, I went to the tennis club for my 2nd evaluation as to my ability to do "tennis court running," very different from jogging on a treadmill, or track. The result of the evaluation was very different from the 1st one. The same coach as before tested me. We warmed up, then he did the same as before. He stood at the net and tossed balls 4 or 5 paces from me, so that I had to run to return the ball. This time, my right ankle didn't buckle, like last time. We found that when moving to my left, I reached the ball easily, but when moving to the right, my ankle was fine, but I was almost a full step slower, which was all about footwork. In other words, something that could be fixed on the court. The bottom line is that I had my first session with the coach, who I will refer to as Coach K, 3 weeks ago. In that first session, I just hit forehands and backhands, tossed a stride or two away from me. Two weeks ago, we had our 2nd session, and we went back to the 5-pace distance. When Coach K tossed the ball 5 paces to my left, I naturally took my first step with my right foot, and had no trouble striking the ball. However, when he tossed the ball 5 paces to my right, I naturally took my first step with my left foot, which, because of my weaker right side, slowed down my second step, causing me to get to the ball late. The bottom line was that once I changed to a right first step, when moving right, I reached the ball at the correct time. So, we fixed my problem in one session. During last week's lesson, Coach K stood on his side of the court and hit me balls, with me not knowing which side he was going to hit to, which forced me to be ready to move in either direction, which was what I wanted. I cannot express the feeling of joy I felt being able to move from side to side with only mild effort, not worrying about falling, and generally having a great time. I know that tennis is not the entirety of my life, and there are hundreds of things that I may or may not be able to do now, that I did effortlessly before, but, a big part of life is about attitude, and I like to think that most of the reason I am standing on a tennis court now is because of my attitude. This week marks 11 months since my stroke, and this week, Coach K and I are going to play a match. I know he will take it easy on me, after all he is a Pro. But the fact remains, I will play a tennis match 11 months after suffering a stroke which completely paralyzed my right side. A full month ahead of schedule. More importantly, I kept the promise I made to myself on Day One.

Tennis, anyone?

ABOUT THE AUTHOR

    T.J. Bullit is the pen name of the man who in 2021 suffered the stroke documented in this book. The root cause of his stroke will forever remain unknown. He is the father of four and the grandfather of four. He is ex-military, and has the discipline to have stuck to a total fitness lifestyle all of his adult life. He is an accomplished martial artist and, as mentioned numerous times in the book, an avid tennis player. He also, as mentioned in the book is a singer, guitarist, and songwriter and does have a small production studio in his home. He stands 5'7", and weighs in at a solid 150 pounds from years of weightlifting. His general health and overall physical condition prior to his stroke, as briefly described in the Introduction, were excellent. He can be reached at t.bullit@yahoo.com.

Made in United States
Orlando, FL
28 July 2022